Lean Six Sigma

POCKET GUIDE

LEAN

CONTROL DEFINE
IMPROVE ANALYZE MEASURE

RATH & STRONG
Management Consultants
Founded in 1935

ISBN 0-9746328-6-4

September 2007

Rath & Strong Management Consultants
45 Hayden Avenue
Suite 2700
Lexington, Massachusetts 02421
Tel: 781/861-1700
www.rathstrong.com

BY
Mary A. Williams
Charlene Adair

DESIGN/PRODUCTION
Jean F. Drew

Foreword

Rath & Strong's new *Integrated Lean Six Sigma Pocket Guide* is the newest contribution from the *Wall Street Journal* best-selling publisher of the world's leading Lean and Six Sigma pocket guides. While today at the forefront of business process improvement at companies worldwide, as a firm with a unique pioneering history, Rath & Strong brings insight, depth, and hands-on, practical experience to the integration of these leading methodologies. This pocket guide is dedicated to our innovative colleagues who transformed quality in the United States.

Rath & Strong pioneered Lean by helping bring this powerful concept to the United States in the 1960s and 70s, when Rath & Strong consultants Arnold O. Putnam and Henry Parker introduced work cells modeled after the Toyota Production System (TPS).

At Motorola in the 1970s, our esteemed colleague, Dorian Shainin, and other Rath & Strong consultants, worked with Bill Smith, under the direction of Bob Galvin, as Motorola first began developing what is today called Six Sigma.

In the 1980s, Rath & Strong consultant Charlene Adair led pioneering work in the introduction of Just-in-Time and its integration with behavioral areas, while Rath & Strong vice president Mary Williams has led in the integration of Lean and Process Redesign with Quality — what is now commonly referred to as Lean Six Sigma. Today, Rath & Strong leads the field globally.

Our long history is based on years of getting results for our clients — many of the world's most successful organizations.

But the real difference lies in our innovative approach, and how we work with clients. In building partnerships with our clients, we transfer the skills needed to guide change and achieve enduring results. We are proud to introduce *Rath & Strong's Integrated Lean Six Sigma Pocket Guide* to support the work of Lean Six Sigma teams and initiatives globally.

Dan Quinn
President and Chief Executive Officer
Rath & Strong Management Consultants

TABLE OF CONTENTS

TABLE OF CONTENTS

Tool Name	Chapter Number and Page	Each tool in this list is categorized as Lean or Six Sigma. It shows the phase of DMAIC where the tool is most often used.		
		Six Sigma	Lean	DMAIC
5S and the Visual Workplace	5/203		●	I
Affinity Diagram	2/20	●	●	D, I
Brainstorming	4/131	●	●	A
Business Case	2/13	●		D
Cause-and-Effect Diagram	4/132	●	●	A
Charter	2/12	●	●	D
Control Charts	6/237	●		M, A, I, C
Cell Design 1: Select the Loop	4/113		●	A
Cell Design 2: Time & Work Analysis	4/117		●	A
Cell Design 3: Evaluate Equipment	4/123		●	A
Cell Design 4: Design Cell Layout	5/179		●	I
Cell Design 5: Determine Staffing	5/188		●	I
Cell Design 6: Plan the Operation	5/196		●	I
Cell Design 7: Implement	5/225		●	I
Cell Design 8: Debug	5/229		●	I
Cell Design 9: Maintain Improvement	6/234		●	C

Tool Name	Chapter Number and Page	Each tool in this list is categorized as Lean or Six Sigma. It shows the phase of DMAIC where the tool is most often used.		
		Six Sigma	Lean	DMAIC
Cell Design 10: Close Project	6/254	●	●	C
CTQ (Critical to Quality)	2/24	●	●	D
Current State Value Stream Map	3/42		●	M
Data Collection	3/33	●	●	D, M, A, I, C
Debugging	5/229		●	I
Design of Experiments	4/158	●		A, I
Ergonomics	5/214		●	I
FMEA	3/36	●	●	M, I
Frequency Plot	3/81	●		M, A, I, C
Future State Value Stream Map	4/99		●	A
Gage R & R	3/58	●		M
Generate Solutions	5/176	●	●	I
Hypothesis Tests	4/142	●		A
Kaizen	5/222		●	I
Kano Model	2/22	●		D
Little's Law	3/50		●	M
Operational Definitions	3/41	●	●	M
Pareto Chart	3/88	●		M, A, I, C
Prioritization Matrix	3/35	●		M, I
Process Capability	3/89	●		M, I

Tool Name	Chapter Number and Page	Each tool in this list is categorized as Lean or Six Sigma. It shows the phase of DMAIC where the tool is most often used.		
		Six Sigma	Lean	DMAIC
Process Mapping	3/52	●	●	D, M, I
Process Sigma	3/91	●		M, I
Product Family Matrix	2/26		●	D
Regression Analysis	4/152	●		A
Rolled Throughput Yield	2/19	●		D
Sampling	3/62	●		M, A, I, C
Scatter Plots	4/138	●		A
SIPOC	2/17	●	●	D
Sphagetti Diagram	2/28		●	D
Stakeholder Management	2/16	●	●	D
Standardization	6/234	●	●	C
Standardized Work	5/196	●	●	I
Stratification	3/39	●		M, A, I
Takt Time	4/100		●	A
Time Series Plots (Run Charts)	3/71	●		M
VOC (Voice of the Customer)	2/20	●	●	D

THE INTEGRATION OF SIX SIGMA AND LEAN: OVERVIEW

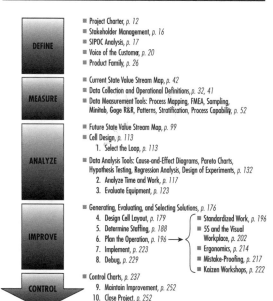

DEFINE
- Project Charter, *p. 12*
- Stakeholder Management, *p. 16*
- SIPOC Analysis, *p. 17*
- Voice of the Customer, *p. 20*
- Product Family, *p. 26*

MEASURE
- Current State Value Stream Map, *p. 42*
- Data Collection and Operational Definitions, *p. 32, 41*
- Data Measurement Tools: Process Mapping, FMEA, Sampling, Minitab, Gage R&R, Patterns, Stratification, Process Capability, *p. 52*

ANALYZE
- Future State Value Stream Map, *p. 99*
- Cell Design, *p. 113*
    1. Select the Loop, *p. 113*
- Data Analysis Tools: Cause-and-Effect Diagrams, Pareto Charts, Hypothesis Testing, Regression Analysis, Design of Experiments, *p. 132*
    2. Analyze Time and Work, *p. 117*
    3. Evaluate Equipment, *p. 123*

IMPROVE
- Generating, Evaluating, and Selecting Solutions, *p. 176*
    4. Design Cell Layout, *p. 179*
    5. Determine Staffing, *p. 188*
    6. Plan the Operation, *p. 196* →
        - Standardized Work, *p. 196*
        - 5S and the Visual Workplace, *p. 202*
        - Ergonomics, *p. 214*
        - Mistake-Proofing, *p. 217*
        - Kaizen Workshops, *p. 222*
    7. Implement, *p. 223*
    8. Debug, *p. 229*

CONTROL
- Control Charts, *p. 237*
    9. Maintain Improvement, *p. 252*
    10. Close Project, *p. 252*

OVERVIEW

In general, customers are concerned about cost, quality, and time. Therefore, those involved in improvement projects need the tools of both **Lean** and **Six Sigma** to respond to these concerns most effectively.

LEAN IS

- a way to understand value from the viewpoint of the customer and eliminate **waste** — activities that don't add value.
- a methodology to increase velocity and create a continuous flow of value-adding activities, pulled by the customer.
- a set of tools to continuously improve this flow.

LEAN IS NOT:

- Less space
- Fewer people
- Limited resources
- Efficiency no matter what
- Not enough supplies
- Giving the customer the bare minimum

Lean eliminates waste and creates continuous flow in any **Value Stream**. A Value Stream is all of the actions, both value-creating and non value-creating, required to bring a product from order to delivery. This includes actions to process information and transform the product. Lean creates a foundation for continuous improvement within the Value Stream.

SIX SIGMA IS

- a rigorous performance improvement approach.
- a customer-focused, data-driven approach to understanding process variation (stability) and process capability.
- a universal problem-solving methodology (DMAIC).
- a performance target of 3.4 defects per million opportunities.

HOW LEAN WORKS WITH SIX SIGMA

Lean and Six Sigma are complementary, since Six Sigma eliminates variation and defects, both of which can create havoc when trying to eliminate waste and create continuous flow. And, of course, the opposite can occur as well: Having waste and lack of continuous flow can cause us to eliminate variation and defects in a process that doesn't even add value!

DMAIC

DMAIC is an acronym meaning **D**efine, **M**easure, **A**nalyze, **I**mprove, **C**ontrol. This is the methodology followed in Lean Six Sigma. It is a rigorous, structured approach to processs improvement. Each of the phases of DMAIC has a logical connection to the previous phase as well as to the following phase.

DEFINE

The first phase is Define. In this phase, the team gets clear marching orders through a project charter that includes the business case. The products (goods or services) are viewed to determine a product "family" in order to define what value stream will be mapped in the Measure phase. The team also achieves a common understanding of the process to be improved through a high-level process map. Lastly, the team becomes acquainted with what is important to the customer(s).

MEASURE

Once the team has understood those items mentioned in the Define phase, it needs to understand the extent of the problem being studied. Data will be gathered on the baseline performance and a current state value stream map will be drawn. The data will be analyzed in such a way as to attempt to recognize the location of the problem. This will allow the team to focus its effort.

ANALYZE

A future state value stream map is created, and a "loop" or section of that map is selected for the improvement project. It is now that the team will determine the root cause(s) of the problem in the loop selected. The problem can be any combination of time, quality, and cost. Too often we "fix" problems without finding a root cause and wonder why we do not get the results we hoped for. Root causes are proved with data.

IMPROVE

Now that the team knows the root cause of the problem, it can design an improvement to the process. In addition to designing the improvement, the team will test the improvement and plan for full-scale implementation.

CONTROL

It will now be imperative that the team design a system that will maintain the gains that it has achieved. This control management system will be designed and tested, and the new process will be standardized. The team can then write a final report, including lessons learned and opportunities for replication.

There is a wonderful logic to the DMAIC methodology. A team moves from understanding the process it is to improve, including what is important to the customer, to using data to document the extent of the problem. Then we find the root cause, and we design a process that will repair the process, test that we in fact have fixed the problem, and then ensure that we hold the gains by continuing to measure the process.

DEFINE

- Project Charter
- Stakeholder Management
- SIPOC Analysis
- Voice of the Customer
- Product Family

MEASURE

- Current State Value Stream Map
- Data Collection and Operational Definitions
- Data Measurement Tools: Process Mapping, FMEA, Sampling, Minitab, Gage R&R, Patterns, Stratification, Process Capability

ANALYZE

- Future State Value Stream Map
- Cell Design
  1. Select the Loop
- Data Analysis Tools: Cause-and-Effect Diagrams, Pareto Charts, Hypothesis Testing, Regression Analysis, Design of Experiments
  2. Analyze Time and Work
  3. Evaluate Equipment

IMPROVE

- Generating, Evaluating, and Selecting Solutions
  4. Design Cell Layout
  5. Determine Staffing
  6. Plan the Operation $\longrightarrow$
  7. Implement
  8. Debug

  - Standardized Work
  - 5S and the Visual Workplace
  - Ergonomics
  - Mistake-Proofing
  - Kaizen Workshops

CONTROL

- Control Charts
  9. Maintain Improvement
  10. Close Project

Phase 1: DEFINE

In Phase 1: Define, you will be setting project goals and boundaries based on knowledge of your organization's business goals, customer needs, and the process that needs to be improved to reduce lead time, defects, and variation.

- Project Charter
- Stakeholder Management
- SIPOC Analysis
- Voice of the Customer
- Product Family

DEFINE

MEASURE

ANALYZE

IMPROVE

CONTROL

The tools most commonly used in the Define phase are:
1. Project charter (including the business case)
2. Stakeholder analysis and communications plan
3. SIPOC
4. Rolled Throughput Yield
5. Voice of the Customer
6. Affinity Diagram
7. Kano Model
8. Critical-to-Quality (CTQ) Tree
9. Product Family Matrix
10. Spaghetti Diagram

PROJECT CHARTER

A **project charter** is an agreement among the Champion, Black Belt(s), and eventually the project team about what is expected. The charter helps you
- clarify what is expected of you, the team, and ultimately the Process Manager or Value Stream Leader.
- keep the team focused.
- address issues that are critical to the project's success.
- uncover potential issues or snags.
- define interaction points and frequencies.
- begin the dialog of issues and shared responsibilities.
- transfer the project from the Champion to the team.

ELEMENTS OF A CHARTER:
- Problem Statement
- Measurable Goals/Objectives
- Business Case
- Project Scope

12

- Roles/Resources
- Schedules/Deliverables

Problem Statement
A **Problem Statement** should not contain cause or solution.

The Charter's Problem Statement answers:
- What problem is the team addressing?
- What is the baseline performance?
- What is the magnitude and trend of the problem?

Goals and Objectives
Goals should be SMART — an acronym for:
Specific, **M**easurable, **A**chievable, **R**elevant, and **T**imely

For each goal identify the metric, baseline performance, current performance, goal, and entitlement. (By entitlement we mean the best performance that we can achieve using the resources on hand at the time.)

BUSINESS CASE

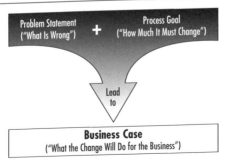

HARD AND SOFT SAVINGS OF LEAN SIX SIGMA

	HARD	**SOFT**
IMMEDIATE	• Cost reduction • Additional Customer sales • Cash flow	• Cost avoidance • Customer impact • Risk reduction
LONG-TERM	• Cost reduction • Additional Customer sales	• Increased capabilities • Employee satisfaction • Customer impact • DFSS benefits*

* DFSS: Design for Six Sigma

Project Scope

A **project scope** is a specific description of the scope of the project/value stream that clearly defines the boundaries (beginning and ending points).

The scope should

- be at an actionable level.
- indicate any constraints for the team.
- specify products, locations, etc., to focus on.

Roles and Responsibilities

- Ensure project has a Champion, Value Stream Leader/Process Owner, and Coach.
- Involve Black Belts or Green Belts in identifying team members.

- Ensure team includes a combination of people who
  - have detailed knowledge of the target process.
  - have the technical skills required to complete the project.
  - can help build commitment and buy-in to the project (and its outcomes) by virtue of being involved from the start.
- Identify "subject matter experts" who may be needed on a part-time basis...don't forget Finance, IT, HR....
- Include members who can represent internal and external customers and suppliers.
- Include other support, such as help acquiring data, travel, special supplies, new hardware or software, etc.

Schedules and Deliverables

A **Project Plan** is used in the Charter to communicate a project's major deliverables and status. It identifies actions necessary to achieve project objectives.

Step Name	Days	July	Aug	Sept	Oct	Nov	Dec	Jan	Feb	Mar
DEFINE	10–20 days	✗								
MEASURE	30–40 days	✗	✗							
ANALYZE	30–40 days			✗						
IMPROVE	15–25 days				✗					
IMPLEMENT	30–45 days					✗	✗			
CONTROL	31 days							✗		

STAKEHOLDER MANAGEMENT

A DMAIC project will require a fundamental change in the process. In an effort to mitigate the resistance to change when the improvement is implemented, it is crucial to identify the stakeholders early on, and to develop a communication plan for each of them. Typical stakeholders include managers, people who work in the process under study, upstream and downstream departments, customers, suppliers, and finance. Regular communication can create more buy-in, identify better solutions, and avoid pitfalls.

Effective stakeholder management involves:
- Stakeholder identification
- Stakeholder analysis
- Stakeholder planning

How to identify stakeholders
- Identify the "obvious" people/groups.
- Identify the "not-so-obvious" people/groups.
- Use project activities to identify other potential people/groups.
- Complete your list by considering managers and direct reports.

STAKEHOLDER ANALYSIS

Analyzing stakeholders involves understanding as much as you can about them and the situation they are in, so that you can plan how to work with them in the most effective way possible.

STAKEHOLDER PLANNING

Regular communication must be planned for each stakeholder, and must be in a medium that each desires. Some might want a half-page memo, others a phone call, still others a formal presentation.

AN EXAMPLE OF A STAKEHOLDER MAP

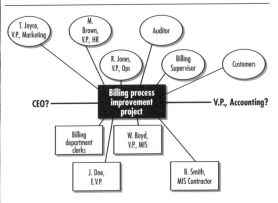

Those above the project in circles are in favor of the project. The closer to the project, the more influence they have. Those below the project in squares are against it. We are not yet sure whether those along the horizontal line (CEO and VP Accounting) are aligned with the project, so they are placed in a "neutral" position for now.

SIPOC

A SIPOC is a high-level process map that includes **S**uppliers, **I**nputs, **P**rocess, **O**utputs, and **C**ustomers. Quality is judged based on the output of a process. The quality of the output is improved by analyzing input and process variables.

SIPOC is a very effective communications tool. It ensures that the team members are all viewing the process in the same way. It also informs leadership of exactly what the team is working on. Therefore, it should be done in the early stages of the project.

The process is bounded with this tool. The process is mapped at a high level (4–7 steps). Then working from the right, identify the output, customers, the input, and the suppliers. An example follows.

DRY CLEANING & LAUNDRY SIPOC ANALYSIS

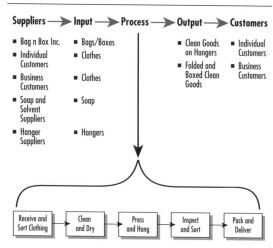

Suppliers →	Input →	Process →	Output →	Customers
▪ Bag n Box Inc.	▪ Bags/Boxes		▪ Clean Goods on Hangers	▪ Individual Customers
▪ Individual Customers	▪ Clothes			▪ Business Customers
▪ Business Customers	▪ Clothes		▪ Folded and Boxed Clean Goods	
▪ Soap and Solvent Suppliers	▪ Soap			
▪ Hanger Suppliers	▪ Hangers			

Receive and Sort Clothing	Clean and Dry	Press and Hang	Inspect and Sort	Pack and Deliver

HOW TO CREATE A SIPOC

- Name the process.
  - What is the purpose?
- Clarify start and stop (boundaries) of the process.
- Identify, name, and order the major process steps.
- List key outputs and customers.
  - What product or service does this process make?
  - Who uses the output?
- List key inputs and suppliers.
  - What material and/or information is necessary to produce the output?
  - Where does it come from?

ROLLED THROUGHPUT YIELD (RTY)

Often in manufacturing, the calculation of rolled throughput yield can help to focus the problem. RTY is the portion of the product that moved through the entire value stream right the first time. Here is an example.

Rolled Throughput Yield (RTY) = (0.99) (0.99) (0.57) (0.90) (0.95) = 48%

The team should focus on step 3, which has a 57% yield.

VOICE OF THE CUSTOMER

We cannot assume that we know what customers want or what they think is important. We actually have to ask them. Otherwise, we will not know what to produce or how to provide our service. In order to do that, we need to know who the customers are and what we want to ask them. In many cases we have customer data on hand in the form of complaints, service calls, returns, etc. In some cases we will have to be more pro-active and conduct such things as interviews, focus groups, and surveys.

AFFINITY DIAGRAMS

An **Affinity Diagram** is a tool that organizes language data into related groups. It stresses creative or intuitive thinking and can be used throughout all the DMAIC phases.

CREATING AN AFFINITY DIAGRAM

- Write ideas on sticky notes.
- Post ideas on a wall or flip-chart.
- Allow team members to move the notes into clusters that make sense.
  - Work quickly.
  - No talking
  - Allow people to move ideas back and forth.
  - Allow clusters within clusters.
  - Name each cluster.

WHY CREATE AN AFFINITY DIAGRAM?

- Encourages breakthrough thinking
- Helps to identify patterns in data
- Facilitates a lot of ideas
- Can be used to organize ideas, issues, and opinions
- Encourages ownership of results

EXAMPLE OF AN AFFINITY DIAGRAM:

Accurate Orders
• On-line catalog up-to-date and correct
• Pull-down menus on order form match on-line catalog item number and price
• Correct links to order form

Order Picking
• Orders picked up within 5 minutes
• Bin numbers match item numbers

Quick Delivery
• Order shipped within 2 hours
• Order received next business day

KANO MODEL

Noriaki Kano is a renowned Japanese expert in total quality management. His practical experience with understanding customer requirements led him to define three categories of customer needs.

- **Must Be**: These needs are expected by the customer. If they are unfulfilled, the customer will be dissatisfied, but even if they are completely fulfilled the customer would not be particularly satisfied (e.g., payment of insurance claims).

    Customers are likely to mention "must be" needs only if they are not being met (e.g., clean hotel room).

- **More Is Better**: These needs have a linear effect on customer satisfaction — the more these needs are met, the more satisfied these customers are (e.g., prompt payment of insurance claims).

- **Delighters**: These needs do not cause dissatisfaction when not present but satisfy the customer when they are (e.g., insurance payments made directly to the vendor so that a policyholder does not have to file a claim). Customers rarely identify what will delight them, since it is in part the unexpectedness of the feature or service that makes it a delighter. Once customers come to expect the feature, it quickly becomes a Must Be.

This is what the Kano Model looks like:

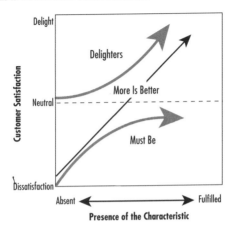

THE KANO MODEL AND VOC

- Must Be characteristics are typically not mentioned by customers unless they are absent.
- More Is Better characteristics are usually discussed by customers.
- Delighter characteristics are usually not mentioned as the customer has not thought of them and is not dissatisfied with their absence.

CTQ (CRITICAL-TO-QUALITY) TREE

- CTQs are the translation of customer needs into quantified requirements for our product/service.
- CTQs are critical requirements placed on the product/service.

EXAMPLE OF A CTQ TREE:

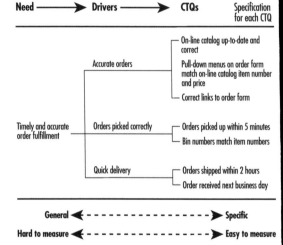

A tree diagram can help you move from a "Need" to a "CTQ." In some cases, you will be able to go directly from the Need to the CTQ, while in other cases you may need to drive down through several layers of the tree in order to discover the underlying CTQs.

VOC	CTQ	Defect Definitions	Measure
"Your cars take too long to start."	Engine starts fast	Engine start time is greater than 3 seconds	Time from turning of key to sustained idle (in seconds)
"Do you have more than one person answering the phones there?"	Call answered promptly	Any call answered after third ring	Time from beginning of first ring to greeting

Once you have identified customer needs, you must identify what they consider to be Critical to Quality requirements; features by which they evaluate the quality of your service or product.

HOW TO CREATE A CTQ TREE:

- List the customer needs.
- Identify the major drivers for these needs (major means those which will ensure that the need is addressed).
- Break each driver into greater detail.
- Stop the breakdown of each level when you have reached the level of detail where you can measure whether you meet the customer need or not.

SETTING SPECIFICATIONS FOR CTQS

- Specifications often come from technical requirements in a manufacturing environment.
- In service and transactional environments, set specification limits where customer satisfaction begins to drop dramatically.
- Specifications can either be one-sided or two-sided.

PRODUCT FAMILY MATRIX

IDENTIFYING A PRODUCT FAMILY TO DETERMINE THE PROJECT SCOPE

DETERMINING THE PROJECT SCOPE

Determining the project scope is a bit like peeling the onion — one layer at a time. We can use a high-level SIPOC, which identifies the Supplier, Inputs, Processes, Outputs, and Customers, or a strategic Value Stream Map for the entire company, to "peel the onion" down to a manageable level.

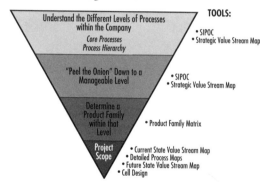

Then, we identify Product Families within that level to determine a manageable scope for an improvement project.

WHAT IS A PRODUCT FAMILY?

A Product Family is a group of products that use the same or similar processing steps and equipment within the selected Value Stream, or scope. Product Families are the most effective unit for analyzing a Value Stream.

WHY IDENTIFY PRODUCT FAMILIES?

We identify Product Families to better define a Value Stream project scope, to identify specific inputs and outputs, and to get greater detail when we begin mapping the Value Stream. This allows us to set more specific improvement goals and focus on a manageable process improvement project. After all, if a Value Stream represents the flow of the product, the Value Stream Map (VSM) cannot map more than one product flow with any clarity.

USING A PRODUCT FAMILY MATRIX TO IDENTIFY PRODUCT FAMILIES

Steps to identify Product Families using a Product Family Matrix include:

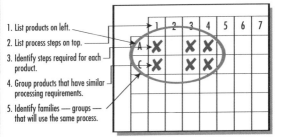

1. List products on left.
2. List process steps on top.
3. Identify steps required for each product.
4. Group products that have similar processing requirements.
5. Identify families — groups — that will use the same process.

Process steps need to be listed in enough detail to show differences in processes, but not at the work step level. Products do not have to have exactly the same process steps to be in the same family, but they should have mostly the same processing steps. Additional data may be required to determine if differences are significant or not.

Products should be listed in enough detail to show differences in the processes each passes through. **Products** are fairly easy to identify in a manufacturing company — they are usually what the company makes and sells. It is more challenging to determine what the products are in a service or transactional Value Stream. You can easily fall into traps in defining the product!

The following is an example of a completed Product Family:

Identify Process Steps	Rearrange; Find Families

Products do not have to have **exactly** the same processes to be in the same family, but should be close.

VALIDATING PRODUCT FAMILIES

A **Spaghetti Diagram** can be used in most Value Streams to validate product families. A Spaghetti Diagram shows the actual path taken by a product as it travels through the processes of the Value Stream.

By differentiating each product on a physical layout (or transactions through different systems and departments), it is easy to verify which products travel through primarily the same process path. This is also a good test for the level of detail chosen to determine Product Families.

The following chart is an example of a Spaghetti Diagram of four products — A, B, C, and D — each represented by a different type of line, solid or dotted. Given their very different paths through the processes, we can confirm that we have four product families.

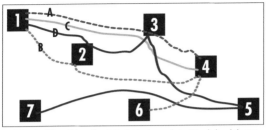

- A "Spaghetti Diagram" shows the actual path taken by a product as it travels through the steps along a value stream. When several products are shown on the same chart, the diagram has the appearance of a plate of spaghetti.

- Begin with a scale layout of the plant or work area. Trace each product separately, using a different color or type of line (solid, dashed, etc.) for each product.

- The paths of products in a product family should be very similar, or there may be more than one product family.

SELECTING A PRODUCT FAMILY

In order to decide what to work on first, identified Product Families need to be prioritized based on criteria such as

- disparity with customer expectations.
- importance to company strategy.
- opportunity for improvement.
- ease or speed of implementation.

Once a Product Family is selected, then it is time to move on to the Measure Phase of DMAIC and Value Stream Mapping.

DEFINE PHASE OUTPUTS

- Project Charter
  - Updated project charter, with revisions highlighted and explained

- Voice of the Customer
  - List of (internal or external) clients of the process
  - Data collection plan for gathering VOC
  - List of CTQ requirements with specification limits
- High-Level Process Map
  - Visual Display of high-level, as-is process map
- Stakeholder management
  - List/map of project stakeholders, how they affect or are affected by the project, probable commitment vs. required commitment
- Product Family
  - Completed product family matrix
  - Product family matrix includes all relevant products and processes.
  - Product family matrix has been confirmed with coach, Champion, VSL.
  - Product family chosen for project
  - Volume variation (within a day, day-to-day, seasonal) has been identified.

CONCLUSION

At the end of the Define Phase, the team has a charter, a high-level process map, and has identified what is critical to quality to the customers. It has also begun stakeholder management. A product family matrix has been developed and a product family chosen in preparation for value stream mapping. The team will move to the Measure Phase to determine baseline performance.

Phase 2: Measure

The Define phase has produced a team charter, an overview of the process to be improved, information on what is critical to quality for customers, a list of stakeholders, and a product family to focus on. Once the team has understood those items mentioned in the Define phase, it needs to understand the extent of the problem being studied. Data will be gathered on the baseline performance. The data will be analyzed in such a way as to attempt to recognize the location of the problem. This will allow the team to focus its effort.

- Current State Value Stream Map
- Data Collection and Operational Definitions
- Data Measurement Tools: Process Mapping, FMEA, Sampling, Minitab, Gage R&R, Patterns, Stratification, Process Capability

The tools used most commonly in the Measure phase are:
1. Control Charts
2. Current State Value Stream Map
3. Data Collection Plan
4. Frequency Plots
5. Gage R&R
6. Pareto Charts
7. Prioritization Matrix
8. FMEA
9. Operational Definitions
10. Process Capability
11. Process Sigma
12. Sampling
13. Stratification
14. Time Series Plots

DATA COLLECTION
Data help us
- separate what we think is happening from what is really happening.
- test theories.
- establish a baseline.
- measure the impact of changes to the process.
- identify cause-and-effect relationships.
- monitor process performance.
- resist jumping to solutions before understanding the root cause of a problem.

CHARACTERISTICS OF PERSUASIVE DATA:

- Relevant: stakeholder cares
- "User-Friendly": stakeholder understands
- Easily Verified: stakeholder can confirm
- Selective: stakeholder isn't overwhelmed
- In Context: stakeholder can compare

In planning for data collection, the most important thing to do is to determine the questions you want answered. Another important thing a team can do in planning for data collection is to draw and label the graph that will communicate the findings before the collection begins. This points you to exactly what data you need. Moreover, it raises questions that you might not have thought of, which you can add to your plan. This will prevent having to go back for data that you had not thought of.

PLANNING FOR DATA COLLECTION

An example of a **data collection plan** follows.

PROJECT: Reduce Laundry Lead Time

What questions do you want to answer?

1.	What is the current lead time?
2.	Is the process stable?
3.	What is the process capability?
4.	How much inventory is there between each step?
5.	What is the set-up time?
6.	What is the process time for each step?

	Data			Operational Definition and Procedures		
What	**Measure Type**	**Data Type**	**How Measured**	**Related Conditions**	**Sampling Notes**	
Lead Time	Output	Continuous	Minutes	Color	Every 7th shirt	
Inventory	Process	Discrete	Count	Steps	Two weeks daily	
Set-up time	Input	Continuous	Minutes	Machine	Two weeks daily	
Process time	Process	Continuous	Minutes	Steps	Every 7th shirt	

What are your plans for Gage R&R? Will conduct Gage R&R on Time and Inventory
How will you plot the data you collect?

1–2	I-MR Chart
3	Process Sigma or Cpk
4	Stratified dotplots
5	Time series plot
6	Stratified dotplots

SELECTING KEY MEASURES
- Data collection and analysis is time-consuming, so it is important to identify the key measures up front.
- Start with the high-level SIPOC.
- Consider using a prioritization matrix and/or FMEA to funnel possible measures to the critical few.

In the equation $Y = f(X_1, X_2, X_3...X_n)$, Y relates to the process output. It tells us how well we are meeting customer needs. X relates to the various input and process variables. We must gain this knowledge in order to improve the process. Understanding the variation in the output variable (Y) requires data about the Xs.

Since data collection can consume a tremendous amount of time, it is critical to focus on the key measures. The high-level SIPOC provides a starting point for identifying possible measures. Other **funneling** tools might be necessary. The two funneling tools, Prioritization Matrix and FMEA follow.

PRIORITIZATION MATRIX
How to construct a prioritization matrix:
- List all output variables.
- Put them in order and assign a weight to each.
- List all input and process variables.
- Evaluate the strength of the relationship between output and input/process variables and assign a correlation factor.
- Cross-multiply weight and correlation factor.
- Highlight the critical few variables.

SAMPLE PRIORITIZATION MATRIX

	Output Variables	Lead Time	Cleanliness	Missing Buttons	Tears	Cost	TOTAL
	Weight	**9**	**9**	**5**	**5**	**1**	
Process/Input Variables	Volume	5	1	5	5	1	105
	Color	1	1	1	1	1	17
	Required starch	1	1	5	5	1	13
	Machine downtime	9	1	1	1	1	21
	Staff out sick, etc.	9	1	5	5	1	93
	Boxes on hand	1	1	1	1	1	21

FMEA

Failure Mode and Effect Analysis (FMEA) is another funneling tool. While it is most commonly used in designing a new product or service, it can be an effective tool for focusing the data collection effort on those input and process variables that are critical for the current process and determining new variables that should be added to the data collection plan. Thus, FMEA can be used in the Measure phase as well as the Improve phase. It is a structured approach to identify, estimate, prioritize, and evaluate risk. It aims at failure prevention.

How to construct a FMEA:

1. List the **process steps**.
2. Adjust severity, occurrence, and detection scales according to the Value Stream.
3. For each step, list the ways it might fail.
4. Rate the severity of each failure.
5. Identify causes of the failures.
6. Rate likelihood causes will occur.
7. Rate ability to detect each failure mode.

8. Multiply the three ratings to get a Risk Priority Number (RPN).

9. The high RPNs are the important variables to measure.

Sample Severity Rating Scale

Severity = likely impact of the failure

Rating	Criteria: A failure could...
10	Cause bodily harm
5	Cause a significant loss of performance
1	Go unnoticed and not affect the performance

Sample Occurrence Rating Scale

Rating	Time Period	Probability
10	More than once a day	>20%
5	Twice a year	≤ 1 per 10,000
1	Once every 5–100 years	≤2 per billion

Sample Detection Rating Scale

Rating	Definition
10	Defect undetectable
5	SPC and manual inspection
1	Defect is obvious and can be kept from reaching the customer

---

THE FMEA FORM

Process Step	Potential Failure Mode	Potential Failure Effects	SEV	Potential Causes	OCC	Current Controls	DET	R P N	Action Recommended	Responsibility	P S E V	P O C C	P D E T
What is the process step?	What can go wrong with the process step?	What is the impact on the customer (the effect on the big Ys)?	How severe is the effect on the customer?	What causes the process step to go wrong — what's the source of failure?	How often does the cause of failure mode occur?	What are the existing controls and procedures that either prevent or detect the cause of the failure mode?	How well can you detect cause or failure mode?	SEV * OCC * DET	What are the actions for eliminating or reducing the occurrence of the cause, or improving detection of the cause or failure mode?	Who is responsible for the action? When should it be completed?			
Clean	Not clean	Customer dissatisfaction	7	Not enough detergent	3	None	10	210	Check detergent inventory every day	Luis	7	1	1
Press	Wrinkled shirt	Customer dissatisfaction	7	Shirt too dry	5	None	10	350	Put timing buzzer in press from with 5 min. warning	Angie	7	1	1

STRATIFICATION

Stratification means dividing data into groups based on key characteristics so that patterns in occurrence of a problem can be identified.

Key Characteristic: some aspect of the data that could explain when, where, and why a problem exists

WAYS TO STRATIFY DATA:

The typical groups are based on:

- People
- Process step
- Product or service
- Machines or other equipment
- Suppliers
- Location
- Time of day, day of week, season

In the Analyze phase we will address how to analyze stratified data. Here we will preview a display of stratified data in an attempt to localize the source of the problem.

The example shows departure times stratified by airport. You can see that ORD has more delays than the others.

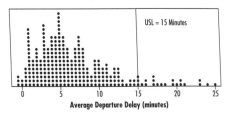

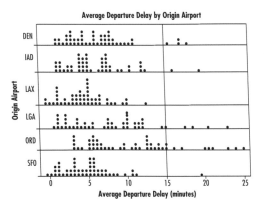

Average Departure Delay by Origin Airport

TYPES OF DATA

Type of Data	How Obtained
Continuous (or "variables")	Measuring instrument or calculation
Discrete: Percentage or Proportion	Count occurrences & non-occurrences
Discrete: Count	Count occurrences
Discrete: Attribute	Observation

Whether a percentage is treated as **continuous data** or **discrete data** depends on how it is calculated. Some percentages, such as % liquid waste, are continuous, since both the numerator and denominator of the percentage are determined by measuring. Percentages determined by counting the number of defects or defectives are best treated as discrete data.

Knowing the type of data is an important issue because

- continuous data give more information.
- the type of data affects the sample size.
- the type of data affects the tools and analytical methods you use.

OPERATIONAL DEFINITIONS

Even simple, one-syllable words such as start and stop need **operational definitions** so that we can rely on the data that have been collected. Do we "start" the clock when the report arrives in my in-box or when I start to work on it? If we are counting errors by type, do all the people in the process call the errors the same thing? Such things need to be clearly defined so that there is no ambiguity. The team is going to change a process based on data, so the data need to be reliable. Operational definitions are an important part of making data reliable. Furthermore, the definitions must be measurable and meaningful.

The features of an operational definition are:

- *Specific*: Different people can use the definition with the same results.
- *Measurable*: A value (numerical or yes/no) can be assigned to a data point.
- *Useful*: It tells you whether or not a customer need has been met.

CURRENT STATE VALUE STREAM MAP

MAPPING THE CURRENT STATE VALUE STREAM TO IDENTIFY WASTE

Why Use a Value Stream Map?

A **Value Stream** is all of the actions, both value-creating and non value-creating, required to bring a product from order to delivery; so a **Value Stream Map (VSM)** is a "picture" of the Value Stream from the product's point of view. This is not a flow chart of what people do, but what happens to the product (a widget, service, electronic record, etc.) as it flows through the Value Stream. A Value Stream Map helps us

- see the entire Value Stream in one picture using a common language.
- work on and improve the bigger picture versus individual processes.
- include information and material flows in addition to the product flow creating a "3-D" picture of the Value Stream.

• identify waste and see the flow, tying together Lean concepts and techniques.

THE LANGUAGE OF VALUE STREAM MAPPING

Consistent icons are needed to create a clear picture of the Value Stream:

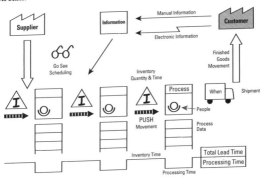

STEPS TO CREATE A CURRENT STATE VALUE STREAM MAP

Guidelines for Drawing the Current State Value Stream Map

• At least one person (preferably the entire team) should walk the entire Value Stream.

• Use pencil and paper or post-it notes and draw by hand to maintain ultimate flexibility.

• Use the standard language (icons).

• Get real data — don't depend on process documentation.

• Erase and modify as you learn more.

• Follow the smallest unit of the product possible — the Value Stream Map maps "one unit" as you have defined it.

You may want to begin with a quick walk through the Value Stream and then go back for details beginning with the customer to ensure that all branches of the Value Stream are captured. Be sure to adhere to all process area etiquette by following normal protocol for visitors and not disrupting the workflow. Be open about the fact that you are evaluating the work process, not the people!

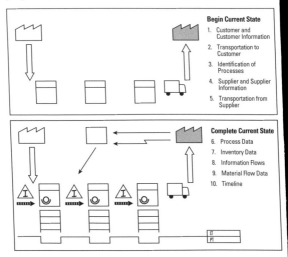

Begin Current State

1. Customer and Customer Information
2. Transportation to Customer
3. Identification of Processes
4. Supplier and Supplier Information
5. Transportation from Supplier

Complete Current State

6. Process Data
7. Inventory Data
8. Information Flows
9. Material Flow Data
10. Timeline

The challenge in collecting data for the Current State Value Stream Map is to collect enough data to baseline the Value Stream and identify opportunities to improve time and flow, but not to collect so much data that you are buried in it for long periods of time.

Steps 1 and 2: Customer and Customer Information, Transportation to Customer

Include:

- A clear specification of value
- Requirements with all relevant detail including quantities, mix, batch/package size, working hours, trends, seasonality, etc.
- Delivery frequency and mode if important
- Any other relevant data

Step 3: Identification of Processes

Includes:

- Process boxes that indicate where material is flowing without significant inventory wait time
- A picture of the flow left to right, including parallel processes and branches

Step 4 and 5: Supplier and Supplier Information; Transportation from the Supplier

Includes:

- The flow for 1 or 2 main suppliers
- Batch/package size and delivery frequency
- Any other relevant data

Below is a Current State Value Stream Map completed through Step 5. This Value Stream could be producing anything: a widget (receive parts, assemble the parts, pack and ship the widget), a service (receive laundry, wash and press the laundry, bag or box laundry and deliver), or a transaction (receive information, input information electronically and make calculations, format conclusions and summary, and e-mail to customer).

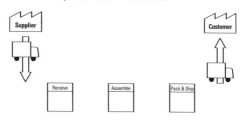

Step 6: Process Data

A Data Collection Plan will be needed as we add the data boxes to each process step. Each data box should include all relevant information about that process. Key data items for consideration are described below. However, data items should not be limited to those below, but should include anything that better describes each process.

Time measurement is extremely important in Lean, since it is a key indicator of waste and flow. **Value-added time** (VA) is the time needed to complete only those work elements (or steps within each process) that are value-added. Of course, an entire process could be deemed non-value-added!

Lead time (LT) is the elapsed time it takes a product (one piece/unit as defined in the Value Stream Map) to move through the defined Value Stream start to finish.

Processing time (PT) is the elapsed time from the time the product enters a process until it leaves that process. In the example Value Stream, the processes are receive, assemble, and pack and ship. Processing time can be considered the lead time for a particular process.

Cycle time (CT) is how often a product is completed by a process. This is a RATE measure, not an elapsed-time measure. We can measure the cycle time at any point in the Value Stream by determining at that particular point the rate at which product is being produced. Cycle time can be calculated for a process by dividing the processing time by the number of people or machines doing the work.

Setup time (SU) is the elapsed time from the last good product unit of the prior batch until the normal production rate is reached on the new batch. Setup time includes activities such as loading, unloading, testing, trial runs, etc.

Uptime (UT) is the percent of time the process actually operates compared to the planned operating time for the process assuming product is available. This measure is typically associated with machine variability. See "Analyzing Equipment Effectiveness" for more detail.

Capacity is the maximum output for a process, and batch size is the quantity of product worked on and moved at one time.

Pack size, or pack-out quantity, is the quantity of product required by the customer for movement or shipment.

Product variation, or **mix**, refers to the number of different product types or models being processed.

Rework Rate is the percent of total product that does not meet the customer's requirement and must be worked on again. This usually requires looping back in the process or a special process.

Scrap Rate is the percent of total product that does not meet the customer's requirement and must be discarded at zero or salvage value.

Defect Rate is the percent of total product that does not meet the customer's requirement and includes both rework and scrap.

Number of people in each process is calculated using a "full time equivalent" calculation. For example, if one person works half time in a process, then the number of people = .5.

Available time per day is the time that the Value Stream can run if there is product to work on. Therefore, if all people in the process take their breaks and/or lunch together, then that time is deducted from the available time. On the other hand, if people stagger their breaks and/or lunch, the Value Stream can run continuously and that time is not deducted.

Typically, setup time and unplanned downtime are not deducted because we want to keep the spotlight on reducing these times. If it applies to the entire value stream, planned downtime is usually deducted, since it is a preventative activity that is designed to keep the process running. However, if it is clear that waste can be eliminated from planned downtime activities, we may decide not to deduct planned downtime from available time. If planned downtime, unplanned downtime, or setup only applies to one process within the Value Stream, deal with it within that process, not the entire Value Stream.

The example on the next page shows the relevant process data for this Value Stream. Note that cycle time was calculated using the processing time and the number of people in each process. The cycle time for this entire Value Stream is 4m — we assume that the prior processes do something to keep up (probably overtime).

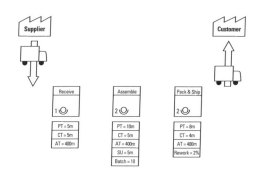

Step 7: Inventory data

Inventory data is very important because if a product is in inventory, it is waiting. Waiting is waste and causes lead times to be longer. Lots of waiting in any process indicates poor product flow. Several categories of inventory are described below.

Raw material (RM) is material, or work, that has not yet been processed by the Value Stream as defined. **Work-in-process** (WIP) is product being processed and **finished goods** (FG) is product that is completed by the Value Stream but awaiting shipment to the customer.

Buffer stock is product held at the downstream end of the Value Stream to protect the customer from starvation if the process cannot produce as needed. **Safety stock** is product held at any point within the Value Stream to prevent downstream processes from starvation if the process cannot produce as needed. **Shipping stock** is product at the downstream end of the Value Stream that is building up for the next shipment.

Inventory turns is a measure of how quickly materials are moving through the Value Stream. It is calculated by dividing the total cost of goods by the average inventory on hand.

Step 8: Information Flows
Information flow tells each process what to make or do next. Examples of information flow are schedules, priorities, forecasts, etc. The question to ask is: "How can we flow information so that one process will make only what the next process needs when it needs it?"

Step 9: Material Flow Data
Movement of the product (or material/information to make the product) is a focus of Lean improvement. Material is typically "pushed" through most Value Streams; Lean helps us create processes whereby the customer "pulls" material through the Value Stream as needed.

Step 10: Timeline
As we have said, lead time is a key indicator of waste and flow in any Value Stream. The timeline in the Value Stream Map tells us how long it take one unit (as defined earlier) to move through the entire Value Stream. Steps to develop the timeline include:

1. Determine the available time — this becomes the baseline time for "a day."

2. Determine the average (or median) production rate per day. This is the "middle" volume that you are basing the Value Stream map on. Variations in that volume will be accounted for later.

3. Determine the processing time for each process in the Value Stream.

4. Determine the time that one unit waits in inventory on average in each inventory location. We use **Little's Law** to translate inventory into lead time:

$$Inventory = Production\ Rate\ x\ Lead\ Time$$
or
$$Lead\ Time = Inventory \div Production\ Rate$$

COMPLETED CURRENT STATE VALUE STREAM MAP (VSM)

The Value Stream Map below illustrates the addition of inventory data, information flows, material flow data, and the timeline. Note that setup time was allocated per unit, or piece, and added to the processing time to create a realistic timeline. Little's Law was used to convert the average inventory in units to lead time. This Value Stream builds 100 units per day using the 400 minutes per day of available time as the baseline. So the production rate is one every four minutes.

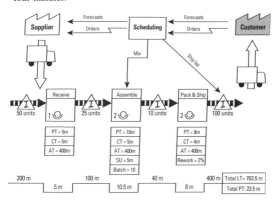

Note that in this example, we allocated the setup time per piece and included it in the timeline calculation. Another option is to assume that the setup time is accounted for in the extra wait time caused by having to accumulate and process a batch of 10 at a time. The important issue is that you have an accurate measure of how long it takes for one unit to move through the Value Stream and that we highlight waste, such as long setups.

PROCESS MAPPING

In most projects it will be necessary to create a more detailed map of the process. Traditionally, we have mapped what people do. In Lean Six Sigma we want to map what happens to the "thing," that is, the product (good or service) that is moving through the process. To understand a process you can:

- Create a map of the process.
- Identify value-added and non-value-added steps.
- Determine lead time and identify bottlenecks.
- Identify complexity or inefficiencies that lead to errors.
- Use the process map as a precursor to FMEA analysis.

WHY USE PROCESS MAPS?

- Creates a common understanding
- Clarifies the steps in a process
- Uncovers problems in the process
- Reveals how the process operates
- Helps you to identify improvement opportunities in a process (complexity, waste, delays, inefficiencies and bottlenecks)

TYPES OF PROCESS MAPS
Activity process map

- Is specific about what happens in the process
- Captures decision points, rework loops and complexity

SAMPLE ACTIVITY PROCESS MAP

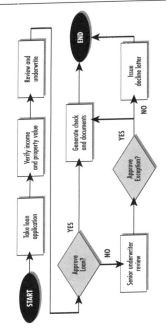

Deployment process map
- Shows detailed steps in a process
- Identifies people or groups involved in each step

SAMPLE DEPLOYMENT PROCESS MAP

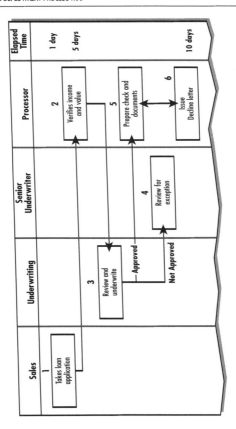

VALUE-ADDED FLOW ANALYSIS

What happens to the thing?

- Looks at the process from the viewpoint of the "thing" going through it ("Staple yourself to the 'thing'.")
- Documents everything that happens to the "thing"
- Used to identify:
  - Non-value added steps
  - Lead time
  - Other process problems
  - Best done by actually "walking the flow"

AN EXAMPLE OF VALUE-ADDED FLOW ANALYSIS

Step	Time	Value-Added
Arrive on Truck		
Wait	2880 min	
Open Mail	2 min	
Move	10 min	
Move to Storage Area	2 min	
Wait	75 min	
Sort	5 min	
Check	10 min	
Number	5 min	5 min
Check Credit	120 min	
Move	10 min	
Wait	30 min	
Enter	2 min	2 min
Print	1 min	1 min
Move	1 min	
Wait	1500 min	
Release		
Totals	**4653 min**	**8 min**

TIME-BASED VALUE-ADDED FLOW ANALYSIS

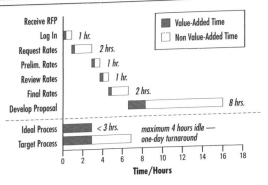

VALIDATING THE MEASUREMENT SYSTEM: GAGE R&R

The goal of validating the measurement system is to minimize controllable factors that could exaggerate the amount of variation in data.

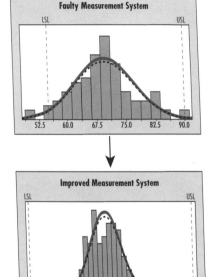

The faulty measurement system (top) makes it appear that the process is beyond the specification limits. Once the measurement system has been improved (bottom), we see that we are well within spec limits.

A **Gage R&R** study is a set of trials conducted to assess the repeatability and reproducibility of your measurement system. This is one way of validating the measurement system.

- Multiple operators measure multiple units multiple times. For example, 4 operators each measure 6 units twice.
- Ideally, Gage R&R tests are blind (operators do not know that this is a special test). They definitely should not know which part they are measuring.
- Analysis of study results reveals how much variation comes from differences in the operators, techniques, or the units themselves.

COMMON PROBLEMS WITH MEASUREMENT SYSTEMS:

- *Bias*: The measurements do not produce the same average value as a standard method (good accuracy if difference is small).
- *Imprecision*: Repeated measurements of the same item produce varying results (good repeatability if difference is small).
- *Not reproducible*: The measurement varies (may be bias or precision) when done by different people, or using different equipment.
- *Lack of resolution*: The measurement system is not precise enough to capture current product variation (5 or more distinct values are necessary to achieve adequate resolution).
- *Unstable over time*: Either the bias or the precision changes over time (good stability if difference is small).

A measurement system consists of:

- Gages
- Procedures
- Operational Definitions
- People

WAYS TO SEE IF THE MEASUREMENT SYSTEM IS ADEQUATE

- *Gage linearity study* — tests for the amount of bias throughout the product range by repeatedly measuring "known" quantities.

- *Gage R&R study* — tests for repeatability by having the same person (or instrument) repeatedly measure the same sample to reveal the variation in the person (or instrument), or for reproducibility by having many people (or instruments) repeatedly measure the same sample.

- *X-bar, R Chart* — tests for stability by having the same person measure the same item over time to reveal special causes that would indicate lack of stability.

Five or more distinct values are necessary to achieve adequate resolution.

ASSESSING THE ACCURACY, REPEATABILITY, AND REPRODUCIBILITY OF A DISCRETE MEASUREMENT SYSTEM

- Discrete data usually involve human judgment.

- A high degree of agreement is needed on how to categorize individual items.

- One way to assess the accuracy, repeatability, and reproducibility of a discrete measurement system is to ask all operators to categorize several known test units and see if they agree. If not, further definition of categories may be needed.

    - Look for 100% agreement.

    - Use disagreements as opportunities to determine and eliminate problems.

As with the Continuous study, the Attribute study is a set of trials where:

- Multiple Operators measure multiple units a multiple number of times.
  - Example: 3 operators each measure 50 units twice (note: the increased sample size).
- "Blindness" is desirable, so ensure that there is sufficient time for the inspectors to forget the previous results, by running the tests on separate days/weeks if necessary.
- Randomization helps to reduce any inspector bias.

PLANNING AND EXECUTING THE STUDY

Identify the process to be studied and which attributes to include in the study.

- Determine the sample size. Because this is attribute data, a larger sample will be necessary. A minimum would be 30 samples, but more is better. The larger the sample size, the smaller the **confidence intervals** in the study. A determination will need to be made to balance sample size and the confidence intervals.
- Collect a set of samples with an equal number of good and bad products or any attribute we want to verify, such as call type or error type. Collect samples that are not obvious as to the correct answer. The study will determine how well the inspector can make the "tough" decision.
- Have subject matter experts or Customers help in the determination of which of the samples are good and which are bad. (This becomes the attribute.)
- Perform at least two trials.

BEGIN DATA COLLECTION

The goal is to ensure a smooth start-up. It requires that you

- train the data collectors.
- error-proof data collection procedures. It helps to pilot and test the data collection forms and procedures.
- be there in the beginning.
- decide how you will display your data.

DEVELOPING A SAMPLING STRATEGY

Sampling: Collecting a portion of the data and using it to draw conclusions when examining all of the data would be too expensive, too time-consuming, or the tests would damage or destroy the items being examined. Sampling is used in every phase of DMAIC where data are collected.

Representative Samples

For conclusions to be valid, samples must be representative.

- Data should fairly represent the population or process.
- No systematic differences should exist between the data you collect and the data you don't collect.

SAMPLING APPROACHES

Sampling Strategy	When to Use It
Random sampling • Every item has an equal chance of being selected	Population

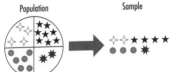

| Stratified random sampling
• Sample represents each group in the same proportion as the population | Population |

Population   Sample

SAMPLING APPROACHES (continued)

Sampling Strategy	**When to Use It**
Systematic sampling • Observations collected at determined intervals	Population or process

Population
or Process

Sample

Preserve Time Order

Subgroup sampling • Groups of observations collected at determined intervals	Process

Process

Sample

9:00   9:30   10:00   10:30

Preserve Time Order

SAMPLING FROM A PROCESS

- Sample systematically or with subgroups (not randomly) across time.

  - Even though random sampling could be applied to stable processes, we use systematic or subgroup sampling and preserve the time order to better represent the process behavior over time.

- Sample from enough time periods to fairly represent the sources of variation in the process.

- Use judgment and knowledge regarding sources of variation to determine how often to sample (every 10th unit, every 7th unit; every day, every month, etc.).
- As a rule, collect small samples more frequently to ensure that the process behavior is represented fairly over time.
- Make a control chart or time plot to determine if the process is stable or unstable.

ESTIMATING SAMPLE SIZE

Selecting a sample size involves trade-offs between precision and cost, and is influenced by:

- Type of data
  - Discrete vs. continuous
- What you want to do:
  - Describe a characteristic for a whole group (mean or proportion).
  - Compare group characteristics (find differences between group means or group proportions).
- What you guess the standard deviation (or proportion) will be
- How confident you want to be (usually 95%)

There is a trade-off between precision, sample size, and cost.

The formulas for sample size were developed for population sampling. They can be applied to process sampling if the process is stable. Since most processes are not stable, the result of the formulas should be used as the smallest sample you should consider.

Sample size to estimate average

$$n = \left(\frac{2s}{d} \right)^2$$

(Where d = precision: ± ___ units)

Sample size to estimate proportions

$$n = \left(\frac{2}{d} \right)^2 (p)(1-p)$$

(Where d = precision: ± ___ units)

Where:

d = precision
n = sample size
p = proportion
s = Standard deviation

PRECISION

Precision is the **range** for an estimate of a characteristic.

- Estimate lead time within ±2 days.
- Estimate percent rejected within ±5%.

The symbol d (for delta) is used to represent precision.

Precision is equal to half the width of a confidence interval.

- A 95% CI = (8, 12) for lead time (in hours) means we are 95% confident the interval from 8 hours to 12 hours contains the average lead time.
- Width of the CI = 4 hours
- Precision = d = 2 hours (= estimate is within ± 2 hours)

PATTERNS IN DATA

Very often the initial data you collect during an improvement project will be data that have a natural time order. After you have looked at the basic statistics, the first step in analyzing time-ordered data is to create a time plot or control chart. The next step is to create a frequency plot of the data and analyze the distribution.

©2007 Rath & Strong/Aon Management Consulting

EXAMPLE OF BASIC STATISTICS

```
Descriptive Statistics: Lead Time

            Total
Variable    Count   Mean   SE Mean   StDev   Minimum   Median   Maximum
Lead Time     84   5.583    0.354    3.242    1.000     5.000    17.000
```

If your data are not time-ordered, chances are you can use either a frequency plot or Pareto chart to analyze it.

- Frequency plots show the distribution of continuous numeric data.
- Pareto charts show the relative frequency or impact of data that can be divided into categories.

The goals of analyzing patterns in data are:

- Understand the relationship between quality and variation.
- Be able to differentiate between common and special cause variation.
- Be able to create and interpret time plots, control charts, frequency plots (histograms), and Pareto charts.
- Understand the difference between control limits (**process stability**) and specification limits (customer requirements, or **process capability**).

UNDERSTANDING VARIATION

- Patterns of variation in time-ordered data (how the data values change from point to point) can provide clues about the source of process problems.
- Quantifying the amount of variation in a process is a critical step towards improvement.
- Understanding what causes that variation helps us decide what kinds of actions are most likely to lead to lasting improvement.

WHAT IS VARIATION?

- There is variation in everything.
- The process will vary over time.
- Procedures will change over time.
- Measurement systems will vary over time.
- Implicit in a Lean Six Sigma project is reducing variation.
- This gives the customer a "predictable future."
- It becomes vital to understand what is driving the variation.

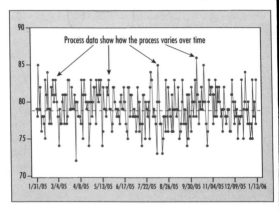

Process data show how the process varies over time

The amount of variation in a process tells us what the process is actually capable of achieving. Specifications tell us what we want a process to be able to achieve, based on customer input. Traditionally, any value between the specifications was seen as good. The new view is that any time a characteristic deviates from the target, there is some loss. The bigger the deviation, the bigger the loss.

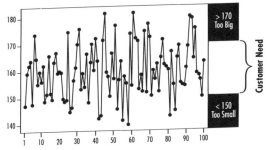

Special cause variation means something different happened at a certain time or place. **Common cause** variation is always present to some degree in the process. The goal is to minimize the variation. It is important to distinguish between special and common cause variation, because each requires a different strategy.

Special cause strategy is:

- Find out what changed.
- Take immediate action to return to the status quo.
- Investigate the cause of the change.
- Prevent that special cause from recurring or, if it was a good special cause, try to make it a standard part of the process.

Common-cause strategy is improving a stable process. The process above is stable, but it does not meet customer needs.

IMPROVING A STABLE PROCESS

- All data are relevant.
- Common cause variation cannot be eliminated altogether, but can be reduced by making fundamental process changes.
- Improving a stable process is usually more complex and requires more time and resources than special cause strategy.

Type of Variation	Type of Action			
	Look for differences between individual points	Take action based on observed differences	Study all the data	Improve the process
Common Cause	Differences aren't important	Increases variation	Helps to understand the process	Decreases variation
Special Cause	Helps to see what's wrong	Decreases variation	Waste of time	May increase variation, no long-term solution

Effective improvement relies on being able to distinguish common cause variation from special cause variation.

- Treating special causes like common causes will result in missing something specific that is increasing variation in the process.
- Treating common causes like special causes usually increases variation.
- Failing to match the action to the type of variation usually makes the variation worse.

TIME SERIES PLOTS

WHY USE A **TIME SERIES PLOT?**
- To look for trends or patterns over time

WHEN TO USE TIME SERIES PLOTS
- Whenever you have time ordered data in order to give you a sense of the variation over time

HOW TO CREATE A TIME SERIES PLOT
- On the vertical line (y-axis), draw the scale of what you are measuring (Yield, Defects, etc.).
- On the horizontal line (x-axis), draw the time or sequence scale.
- Plot the data in time order.

TIME SERIES PLOT FEATURES

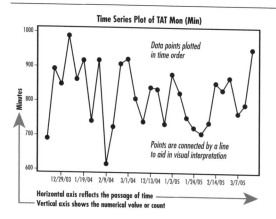

CONTROL CHARTS

(INDIVIDUALS AND MOVING RANGE CHARTS)

A **control chart** plots time-ordered data. Statistically determined control limits are drawn on the plot. The centerline is the **mean**, or **average**.

UNDERSTANDING PROCESS STABILITY

- A control chart is used to determine process stability.
- Control limits are calculated based on ±3 standard deviations from the mean.
- A point beyond the limits is a special cause and indicates a lack of process stability.
- The **range** is the maximum value minus the minimum value.
- There are other indicators of instability as well, which will be discussed in this section.

WHEN TO USE A CONTROL CHART

- As part of the management dashboard to track performance
- To establish baseline performance
- To identify root cause(s)
- To evaluate results of process improvements
- To maintain the gains over time

CONTROL CHART FEATURES

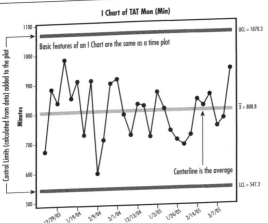

I Chart of TAT Mon (Min)

Basic features of an I Chart are the same as a time plot

Control Limits (calculated from data) added to the plot

Minutes

UCL = 1070.3

$\overline{X}$ = 808.8

Centerline is the average

LCL = 547.3

12/29/03 1/19/04 2/9/04 3/1/04 12/13/04 1/3/05 1/24/05 2/14/05 3/7/05

HOW TO CONSTRUCT CONTROL CHARTS

- Select the process to be charted.
- Determine sampling method and plan.
- Initiate the data collection.
- Calculate the appropriate statistics.
- Plot the data values on the first chart (mean or individuals).

- Plot the range or standard deviation of the data on the second chart (only for continuous data).
- Interpret the control chart and determine if the process is "in control."

HOW TO CALCULATE CONTROL LIMITS

- There are many different control charts, but they have some things in common:
  - The center line is the average.
  - The **control limits** are ±3 standard deviations from the center line.
- Each control chart uses a different estimate of standard deviation.
- It is important that the correct formula is used to calculate limits.

For Individuals charts, the control limits are calculated with the formulas:

- Upper Control Limit = X-bar + 2.66 x R-bar
- Lower Control Limit = X-bar − 2.66 x R-bar

where X-bar is the average of the individual values, and R-bar is the average of a two-point moving range of the individual values.

Formula for R-Chart:

- Upper Control Limit = 3.27 x Average Range

CONTROL CHARTS AND TESTS FOR SPECIAL CAUSES

1. Any data point outside the control limits is a signal of special cause — it signifies something unusual.
2. Eight points in a row on same side of the center line — signifies a shift in the average.

---

3. Six points in a row, all increasing or decreasing — signifies a trend.

4. Fourteen points in a row, alternating up and down — signifies sampling from two sources, bias, or fudged data.

5. Two out of three points (same side) more than 2 sigma from center line — signifies a shift.

6. Four out of five points (same side) more than 1 sigma from center line — signifies a shift.

7. Fifteen points in a row within 1 sigma of center line — signifies reduced common cause variation, change in operational definition, or fudged data.

8. Eight points in a row more than 1 sigma from center line — signifies overcompensation, sampling from different sources, or fudged data.

A **Moving Range chart** can be created at the same time as an individuals chart (see next page).

Moving ranges are the differences between adjacent points; they are used to calculate the control limits. The following chart is measuring turn-around-time for shirts on Mondays.

SAMPLE MOVING RANGE CHART

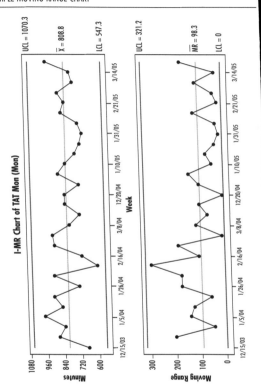

CONTROL CHARTS (X-BAR, R)

When data are collected in rational subgroups, it makes sense to use an **X-bar, R chart**. In the rational subgroup, we hope to have represented all the common causes of variation and none of the special causes of variation. X-bar, R charts allow us to detect smaller shifts than individuals charts. Also they allow us to clearly separate changes in process average from changes in process variability.

Obs	Time	Shirt 1	Shirt 2	Shirt 3	Shirt 4	Range	Average
1	0.427083	0.80607	0.99404	0.82373	0.99308	0.18797	0.90423
2	0.447917	1.06437	1.20776	1.20623	1.07098	0.14339	1.137335
3	0.46875	1.21895	1.12276	1.20429	1.22769	0.10493	1.193423
—	—	—	—	—	—	—	—
—	—	—	—	—	—	—	—
—	—	—	—	—	—	—	—
28	0.572917	1.35633	0.84842	0.71801	1.00658	0.63832	0.982335
29	0.59375	0.89281	0.91148	0.74814	0.88078	0.16334	0.858303
30	0.614583	1.19705	0.76038	1.26645	1.07165	0.50607	1.073883
						Average of the Ranges (R-bar — R)	Grand Average (X-double bar — X̄)
						0.382657	1.024185

Here we are measuring prep time for shirts.
- The range of each subgroup (4 shirts) is calculated and placed on the R-chart.
- The centerline of the R-chart (R-bar) is the average of the ranges.
- The average of each subgroup is plotted on the X-bar chart.
- The average of the averages (Grand Average or X-double-bar) is the centerline.

X-BAR R CHART FEATURES

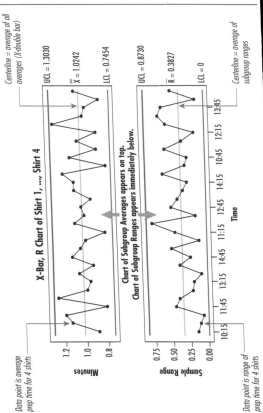

Centerline = average of all averages (X-double bar)

UCL = 1.3030

$\overline{\overline{X}}$ = 1.0242

LCL = 0.7454

X-Bar, R Chart of Shirt 1, ..., Shirt 4

Chart of Subgroup Averages appears on top.
Chart of Subgroup Ranges appears immediately below.

UCL = 0.8730

$\overline{R}$ = 0.3827

LCL = 0

Centerline = average of subgroup ranges

Minutes

Sample Range

Time

Data point is average prep time for 4 shirts

Data point is range of prep time for 4 shirts

CALCULATIONS FOR X-BAR R CHARTS (A DIFFERENT EXAMPLE)

	Control Chart Factors		
n	A_2	D_3	D_4
2	1.880	N/A	3.268
3	1.023	N/A	2.574
4	0.729	N/A	2.282
5	0.577	N/A	2.114
6	0.483	N/A	2.004
7	0.419	0.076	1.924
8	0.373	0.136	1.864

	k_1	k_2	k_3
n_1	16	16	16
n_2	12	15	17
n_3	14	15	16
n_4	13	18	14
n_5	15	16	12
Mean =	14	16	15
Range =	4	3	5

n = # of items in a subgroup   k = # of subgroups

$$UCL_{\bar{x}} = \bar{\bar{x}} + A_2\bar{R} = 15.0 + .577\,(4.0) = 15.0 + 2.308 = 17.3$$

$$\bar{\bar{x}} = \frac{\sum \bar{x}}{\sum k} = \frac{14 + 16 + 15}{3} = \frac{45}{3} = 15.0$$

$$LCL_{\bar{x}} = \bar{\bar{x}} + A_2\bar{R} = 15.0 - .577\,(4.0) = 15.0 - 2.308 = 12.7$$

$$UCL_R = D_4\bar{R} = 2.114\,(4) = 8.5$$

$$\bar{R} = \frac{\sum R}{\sum k} = \frac{4 + 3 + 5}{3} = \frac{12}{3} = 4.0$$

$$LCL_R = D_3\bar{R} = N/A\,(4.5) = N/A$$

$UCL_{\bar{x}} = 17.3$

$\bar{\bar{x}} = 15.0$

$LCL_{\bar{x}} = 12.7$

$UCL_R = 17.3$

$\bar{R} = 4.0$

Subgroup Number

Subgroup Mean

Subgroup Range

Averages will always show less variability than individual values, so you expect the control limits on the X-bar chart to be narrower than limits for individual values. The constants noted above as D_2 and A_2 are the result of having less variability.

INTERPRETING AN X-BAR, R CHART

Because the limits on the X-bar chart are based on the average of the range chart, look at the R-chart first. If there are points beyond the control limits on the R-chart, the limits on the X-bar chart are thrown off. Once the special causes are fixed, recreate the X-bar, R-chart.

Once the R-chart is in control, look for special causes on the X-bar chart.

This applies to I-MR charts as well.

When to Use X-Bar R Charts
X-bar, R-charts are used in high-volume manufacturing. One major assumption is that each subgroup only contains common cause variation. They are seldom applicable in transactional processes because
   • often there is not enough volume.
   • the subgroups contain special cause variation.

Advantages of X-bar, R Charts
The chart allows you to distinguish within subgroup from between subgroup variation. Within variation refers to the range of the subgroups, displayed on the R-chart. Between variation refers to the averages of the subgroups displayed on the X-bar chart.

BUT:
If a special cause appears in each subgroup, the X-bar, R chart is useless.

So think carefully before forming subgroups from
- different operators, machines, shifts, fixtures, etc.
- calendar weeks, months, or quarters.

FREQUENCY PLOTS

A **frequency plot** might be considered a snapshot, while a time series plot or control chart might be considered a video. Nevertheless, it is a useful tool, as there are things that we can see on a frequency plot that we cannot see when we add the time dimension. Of course, we lose the time dimension, so it is best to look at the data both ways (over time and in a frequency plot). Data do not have to be time-ordered to be viewed in a frequency plot.

WHY USE FREQUENCY PLOTS
- This plot shows the variation and shape of the distribution.
- If specification limits are added, this plot helps to judge the process capability.

WHEN TO USE FREQUENCY PLOTS
- To reveal the shape of the distribution
- To reveal the centering and the variation of the data

FREQUENCY PLOT FEATURES

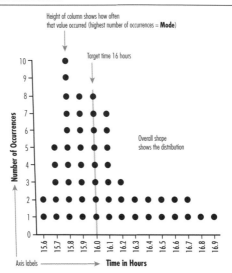

Height of column shows how often that value occurred (highest number of occurrences = **Mode**)

Target time 16 hours

Overall shape shows the distribution

Axis labels ⟶ **Time in Hours**

TYPES OF FREQUENCY PLOTS

There are many types of frequency plots, such as:

- **Histograms**, where data are placed in bins (or buckets) and displayed in bars
- **Dotplots**, where individual data points are displayed
- **Boxplots**, where the data are divided in quartiles

HISTOGRAM

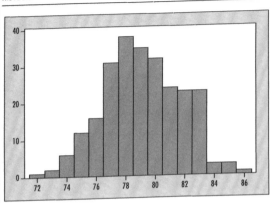

DOTPLOT

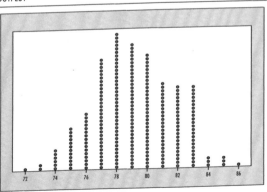

BOX PLOT

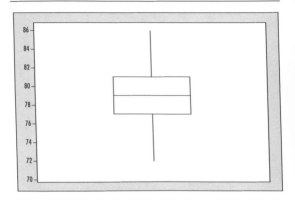

How to Construct a Frequency Plot
- Create an array of the data.
- Count the number of observations.
- Calculate the range (maximum value minus minimum value).
- Determine the number of bins (can start with the square root of the sample size).
- Determine the width of each bin (range divided by number of bins).
- Plot the data.

WHAT TO LOOK FOR ON A FREQUENCY PLOT

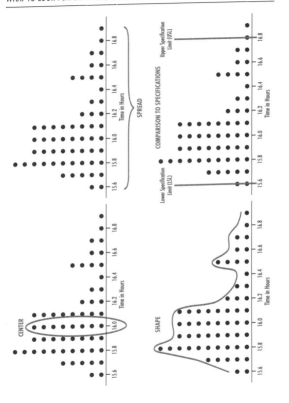

COMMON FREQUENCY PLOT SHAPES

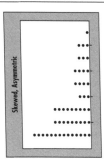

Skewed, Asymmetric

Skewed or asymmetric distribution — often seen in measures of time and money; each has a natural bound at zero. Data can also be skewed in the other direction.

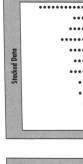

Stacked Data

Stacked data at one point might indicate bias in the measuring device or operator.

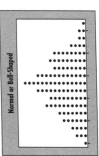

Normal or Bell-Shaped

Normal or bell-shaped curve — this distribution is symmetric.

Bimodal

Bimodal distribution with two peaks — data come from two different sources; e.g., two shifts, two machines, etc.

COMMON FREQUENCY PLOT SHAPES

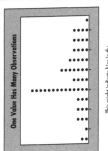

One Value Has Many Observations

This might indicate bias in the measuring device or operator.

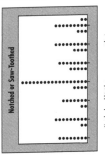

Notched or Saw-Toothed

Notched could indicate measurement device or operator bias.

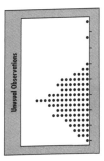

Unusual Observations

Unusual observations seen. These might indicate special-cause variation.

Few Categories

Too few categories indicates rounding by operators or a measurement device without enough precision.

PARETO CHARTS

Some data can best be analyzed by division into categories. A
Pareto chart is a graphical tool that breaks a big problem into
components to identify which are the most important.

PARETO CHART FEATURES

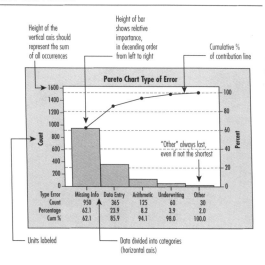

Height of the
vertical axis should
represent the sum
of all occurrences

Height of bar
shows relative
importance,
in decending order
from left to right

Cumulative %
of contribution line

"Other" always last,
even if not the shortest

Units labeled

Data divided into categories
(horizontal axis)

Type Error	Missing Info	Data Entry	Arithmetic	Underwriting	Other
Count	950	365	125	60	30
Percentage	62.1	23.9	8.2	3.9	2.0
Cum %	62.1	85.9	94.1	98.0	100.0

How to Construct a Pareto Chart
- Sort the data in an array from high to low frequency.
- Create a bar for each category.
- Draw a cumulative percent line that displays the percent of
  the total that each category represents.
- Separate the "vital few" from the "useful many."

The Pareto Principle: Holds that a few of the contributors are responsible for the bulk of the problem. Some people call this the 80/20 rule, but we should not be wedded to 80%.

This becomes very useful to us in quality improvement for:

- Selecting projects
- Focusing the effort of a project
- Identifying root causes

WHAT TO LOOK FOR WHEN PERFORMING A PARETO ANALYSIS

Pareto charts are most useful when they show relatively large differences between categories. If your chart doesn't show distinct differences, then you need to explore using alternatives to slicing & dicing your data.

What to Look for:

- Does the Pareto principle hold? Is there one or a few large bars? If all the bars are about the same height, you need to slice the data another way.
- Has the Y axis scale reached the sum of all contributors?
- Does the "Other" category need to be broken down further?
- Are the data representative?

PROCESS CAPABILITY

Process capability measures how much variation there is in a process relative to customer specifications. To increase process capability, process variation must decrease. Less variation provides the following benefits:

- Greater predictability
- Less waste and rework
- Products and services that perform better and last longer
- Improved customer satisfaction

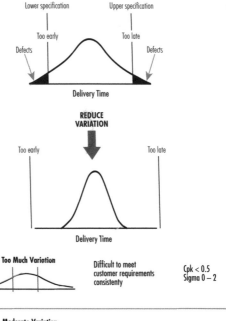

Lower specification   Upper specification

Too early   Too late

Defects   Defects

Delivery Time

REDUCE VARIATION

Too early   Too late

Delivery Time

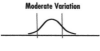

Too Much Variation	Difficult to meet customer requirements consistenty	Cpk < 0.5 Sigma 0 – 2
Moderate Variation	Able to meet customer requirements most of the time	Cpk 0.5 – 1.2 Sigma 3 – 5
Very Little Variation	Almost always able to meet customer requirements	Cpk > 1.5 Sigma 6 or better

Cpk is a measure of process capability. A score below one means that your process exceeds specification limits. A score of 1.0 means that your process is right on the spec limits and will go beyond them if the process shifts at all. Most manufacturing organizations aim for a Cpk of at least 1.33. The higher the Cpk, the less variation from specification limits there is.

The "P" family is process performance and is based on long-term standard deviation.

The "C" family is process capability and is based on short-term standard deviation.

Formulas for calculating process capability
Capability Ratios (Cpk, Cp) (**Ppk**, Pp)

$$CP = \frac{USL - LSL}{6s_{WITHIN}}, \quad CPU = \frac{USL - \overline{X}}{3s_{WITHIN}}, \quad CPL = \frac{\overline{X} - LSL}{3s_{WITHIN}} \qquad s_{WITHIN} = \frac{\overline{R}}{d_2}$$

$$PP = \frac{UL - LSL}{6s_{OVERALL}}, \quad PPU = \frac{USL - \overline{X}}{3s_{OVERALL}}, \quad PPL = \frac{\overline{X} - LSL}{3s_{OVERALL}} \qquad s_{OVERALL} = \frac{s}{C_4}$$

Cpk is the smaller value of CPU and CPL; Ppk is the smaller value of PPU and PPL.

PROCESS SIGMA

It becomes difficult to measure Ppk or Cpk for discrete data. For example, a tablet is crushed or it is not. Process capability can be analyzed using **process sigma**, which is based on yield. The defects and the opportunities are counted. Defects per opportunity are counted and then scaled to one million. Use process sigma for
   • situations where you can count defects and non-defects.
   • process performance in multi-step processes.

THE PROCESS SIGMA SCALE

Process Sigma	Defects per Million Opportunities	Yield
1	691,462	30.9%
2	308,538	69.1%
3	66,807	93.3%
4	6,210	99.38%
5	233	99.977%
6	3.4	99.999966%

Terminology:

CTQ: Critical-to-quality characteristic — performance requirement for a product or service
   • Example: Correct items and quantities are delivered to the customer on-time.

Defect: an event that does not meet at least one of the specified CTQs
   • Example: Shipment was on-time and included the correct items, but quantities were incorrect.

Opportunity: a significant and measurable process parameter that could result in a customer requirement not being met
   • Examples: product availability, order entry, packing, shipping

How to Calculate Process Sigma
For data with at least 5 defects and non-defects:
- Calculate actual first-pass yield.
- Look up yield in process sigma table.

For continuous data that do not meet the criterion of 5 defects and 5 non-defects:
- Estimate process yield by the area under the normal curve.

A Caveat about Process Sigma
- The calculated process sigma level is influenced by the definition of an "opportunity."
- Often, changes in process sigma over time are more indicative of process improvement and customer focus than any given sigma level.

Definitions are Critical.
Apply the concept of operational definitions to both defects and opportunities. Make sure everyone who works with sigma values understands and agrees on critical definitions.
- Defects: Focus on customer requirements.
- Clearly specify what an opportunity is so that all involved understand the definition.

THE PROCESS SIGMA TABLE

Sigma	DPMO	Yield	Sigma	DPMO	Yield
6	3.4	99.99966%	2.9	80,757	91.9%
5.9	5.4	99.99946%	2.8	96,801	90.3%
5.8	8.5	99.99915%	2.7	115,070	88.5%
5.7	13	99.99866%	2.6	135,666	86.4%
5.6	21	99.9979%	2.5	158,655	84.1%
5.5	32	99.9968%	2.4	184,060	81.6%
5.4	48	99.9952%	2.3	211,855	78.8%
5.3	72	99.9928%	2.2	241,964	75.8%
5.2	108	99.9892%	2.1	274,253	72.6%
5.1	159	99.984%	2	308,538	69.1%
5	233	99.977%	1.9	344,578	65.5%
4.9	337	99.966%	1.8	382,089	61.8%
4.8	483	99.952%	1.7	420,740	57.9%
4.7	687	99.931%	1.6	460,172	54.0%
4.6	968	99.90%	1.5	500,000	50.0%
4.5	1,350	99.87%	1.4	539,828	46.0%
4.4	1,866	99.81%	1.3	579,260	42.1%
4.3	2,555	99.74%	1.2	617,911	38.2%
4.2	3,467	99.65%	1.1	655,422	34.5%
4.1	4,661	99.53%	1	691,462	30.9%
4	6,210	99.38%	0.9	725,747	27.4%
3 9	8,198	99.18%	0.8	758,036	24.2%
3.8	10,724	98.9%	0.7	788,145	21.2%
3.7	13,903	98.6%	0.6	815,940	18.4%
3.6	17,864	98.2%	0.5	841,345	15.9%
3.5	22,750	97.7%	0.4	864,334	13.6%
3.4	28,716	97.1%	0.3	884,930	11.5%
3.3	35,930	96.4%	0.2	903,199	9.7%
3.2	44,565	95.5%	0.1	919,243	8.1%
3.1	54,799	94.5%			
3	66,807	93.3%			

MEASURE PHASE OUTPUTS:

- Current State VSM
- Validated measurement system
- Sampling strategy
- Baseline data and calculate process capability
- Process stability
- Stratification to localize problem
- Updated Project Charter

CONCLUSION

At the end of the Measure Phase, the team has a current state value stream map and has collected valid data on the baseline performance. Process stability and capability have been determined. The data have been stratified to localize the problem and the charter has been updated. The team is now prepared to move to the Analyze Phase where it will create a future state value stream map and identify root causes of problems.

Phase 3: Analyze

The Measure phase has produced the baseline performance of the value stream. The first step in the Analyze phase is to create a Future State Value Stream Map. By having stratified the data in the baseline performance, it becomes possible to pinpoint the location or source of problems by building a factual understanding of existing process conditions and problems. That helps focus the problem statement on the loop of the value stream where work

DEFINE

MEASURE

ANALYZE

IMPROVE

CONTROL

- Future State Value Stream Map
- Cell Design
  1. Select the Loop
- Data Analysis Tools: Cause-and-Effect Diagrams, Pareto Charts, Hypothesis Testing, Regression Analysis, Design of Experiments
  2. Analyze Time and Work
  3. Evaluate Equipment

will be done. In the Analyze phase you will develop theories of root causes, confirm the theories with data, and finally identify the root cause(s) of the problem. The verified cause(s) will form the basis for the solutions in the next phase.

The tools used most commonly in the Analyze phase are:
1. Affinity Diagram (*covered in the Define phase*)
2. Brainstorming
3. Cause-and-Effect Diagrams
4. Control charts (*covered in the Measure and Control phases*)
5. Cell Design:
    a. Selecting the Loop
    b. Analyze Time and Work
    c. Evaluate Equipment
6. Data Collection Plan (*covered in the Measure phase*)
7. Design of Experiments
8. Flow Diagrams (*Process Maps — covered in the Measure phase*)
9. Frequency plots (*covered in the Measure phase*)
10. Future state value stream map
11. Hypothesis tests
12. Pareto chart (*covered in the Measure phase*)
13. Regression analysis
14. Sampling (*covered in the Measure phase*)
15. Scatter plots
16. Stratified frequency plots
17. Takt time

CREATING A LEAN FUTURE STATE VALUE STREAM MAP

A Lean Value Stream consists of value-adding activities that produce a product

- exactly as the customer needs it.
- when the customer needs it.
- in the least amount of lead time (best flow).
- at the pace the customer needs it.

A Lean Value Stream has the shortest lead time, the highest quality, and the lowest cost possible. Lean offers a set of concepts and tools that help us build a future state Lean Value Stream one step at a time.

CREATING A FUTURE STATE VALUE STREAM MAP

Steps to create a **Future State Value Stream Map** include:

1. Begin by drawing on the Current State Value Stream map and adding to the data collection plan as you go.

2. Develop the Lean design and draw the new Value Stream map by answering eight questions (see following) in sequence.

3. Create a realistic, doable plan by doing what you can with what you have. In other words, don't plan in a futuristic capability that hasn't been invented yet!

Below are new icons to add to the value stream mapping "language" for Future State Value Stream Mapping.

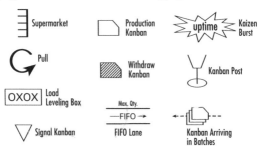

Supermarket	Production Kanban	uptime — Kaizen Burst
Pull	Withdraw Kanban	Kanban Post
OXOX — Load Leveling Box	Max. Qty. —FIFO → FIFO Lane	Kanban Arriving in Batches
Signal Kanban		

EIGHT QUESTIONS TO BUILD A LEAN VALUE STREAM

The following eight questions should be answered in sequence. Each question will be discussed in this chapter.

1. What is the Takt time?
2. Build directly to shipping or to a finished goods supermarket?
3. Where can continuous flow be used?
4. Where are pull systems needed?
5. At what single point (the pacemaker) in the Value Stream is production triggered?
6. How is production mix leveled at the pacemaker?
7. How is production volume leveled at the pacemaker?
8. What process improvements are necessary for the Future State to become a reality?

QUESTION 1: WHAT IS THE TAKT TIME?

Takt time synchronizes the pace of the Value Stream to the pace of customer demand. One of the key wastes discussed in the Introduction is overproduction. **Overproduction** is

- making more than is required by the next process.
- making it earlier than is required by the next process.
- making it faster than is required by the next process.

All of these conditions cause waiting, extra transporting/moving, extra motion, defects — and inventory!

Building to Takt time requires **system efficiency** — everything working at the same rate. An example of this would be a rowing team stroking in perfect harmony to someone's call or a drum. Many Value Streams today focus on **point efficiency** — every person/machine/process is working as fast and hard as possible individually. Imagine how fast the boat would go if each member of the rowing team just paddled as fast and hard as they could!

Question 1 Example
Continuing with the example Current State Value Stream Map from Chapter 3, the Takt time is:

$$\text{Takt Time} = \frac{\text{Available Time per Day (400 min.)}}{\text{Customer Demand per Day (100)}} = 4 \text{ min.}$$

Therefore, the Value Stream needs to build a unit every 4 minutes in order to keep pace with the customer needs.

QUESTION 2: BUILD DIRECTLY TO SHIPPING OR TO A FINISHED GOODS SUPERMARKET?
This question addresses whether we will hold, or accumulate, finished goods or ship finished product as it is produced. If the product is made to standard specifications, then it is possible to accumulate the different standard varieties (or **mix**) before shipping.

In some cases, holding some finished product can help smooth out variation in production volumes.

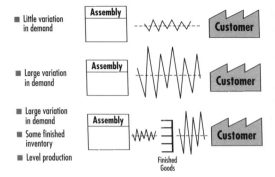

A **supermarket** is a location where a predetermined standard inventory is kept to supply downstream processes or Value Streams. Each item in a supermarket has a specific location, just like shelves in a supermarket (note the icon for supermarket). As an item is taken, a signal is given to provide more.

However, if the product is custom, or specific to a particular customer, it must be shipped as it is produced. All custom products and most service and transactional products would fall into this category. The only accumulation of product in this case is for shipping logistics — this can be a truck load or an electronic batch process that processes transactions.

Question 2 Example
If the Value Stream produces widgets A, B, and C, then we can accumulate extra widgets in a supermarket to ensure that shipment to the customer can occur regardless of which model they choose.

If the Value Stream provides a laundry service, the service of laundering your shirt requires that your clean shirt be shipped to you, not someone else. So, we cannot accumulate extra clean shirts in case yours doesn't get done on time.

QUESTION 3: WHERE CAN CONTINUOUS FLOW BE USED?
Continuous flow results when product is produced and moved from one process step to the next:
- One-at-a-time (as one unit has been defined)
- Without stoppages
- Without scrap
- Without backflow

The benefits of continuous flow include:
- Reduced lead times
- Lower costs
- Improved quality
- Additional stability and flexibility
- Reduced injuries
- Increased employee ownership through involvement

Discontinuous flow can be identified by:
- Inventory accumulation between processes
- Work processed in batches
- Process steps not close to each other
- Evidence of defects, rework, and scrap
- Excessive changeover time and other downtime
- Inconsistent output rates (hour-to-hour, shift-to-shift, etc.)
- Problems not addressed immediately or permanently
- Under- or over-utilized operators
- Imbalance in operator workloads

An **operator balance chart** (OBC) helps compare the cycle time for each person to Takt time. This comparison is also made directly between process cycle times and Takt time. Let's call this a **process balance chart**. This is more appropriate when the cycle of a process depends on equipment as well as/instead of people to do the work. We will discuss equipment cycle time in a later section.

In either case, having a picture of how the Value Stream cycles compared to Takt can help determine where continuous flow might be possible. Here's an operator balance chart for the example process:

SAMPLE OPERATOR BALANCE CHART

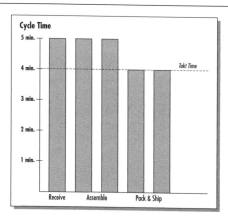

This operator balance chart tells us that Receive and Assemble cannot cycle within Takt and that Pack & Ship can barely cycle within Takt. Another way to measure the number of people required to cycle within Takt time is to use the formula:

$$\text{\# of People} = \frac{\text{Total processing time (23 min.)}}{\text{Takt time (4 min.)}} = 5.75 \text{ people}$$

This calculation verifies that people are working overtime, or they are not able to produce at the rate that the customer needs.

Caution! Do NOT base the future design on this calculation. Improvements and allowances for variation need to be made before determining the number of people needed. The future state design is based on product flow, not keeping people busy.

Question 3 Example
In the example process, we can eliminate the time and cost of overproduction by connecting assemble with pack & ship in a continuous flow. We have also added a supermarket for finished goods assuming that we are producing widgets in three varieties.

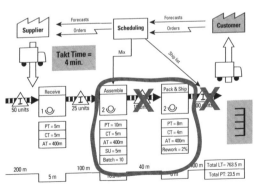

QUESTION 4: WHERE ARE PULL SYSTEMS NEEDED?
When continuous flow is not possible, use pull systems to limit and manage inventory, which improves flow and eliminates waste. **Pull** is a system in which work is done only in response to a signal from the customer or from a downstream process that indicates a need for more product. In some Value Streams, a pull system can also indicate what product is needed.

In any case, when no product is needed, production stops. We do not overproduce! This is one of the most difficult things to do — stop working to solve problems. A Japanese term often used to refer to this concept is **Jidoka**.

The benefits of pull include:
- Team ownership of the flow of product
- Visibility
- Simplicity
- Urgency created to solve problems
- Proper allocation of resources

Use a **supermarket pull system** to control production when continuous flow does not exist and the upstream process must still operate in a batch mode. Possible reasons for this are that the process
- operates very fast or very slow.
- requires setup for product variations.
- is too far away for one unit at a time to be realistic.
- has too much lead time.
- is too unreliable to link directly to another process.

A **kanban** is a signal to produce more or withdraw items in a supermarket pull system. It tells us when, how much, and, possibly, what to produce. Below are some additional icons associated with supermarket pull systems:

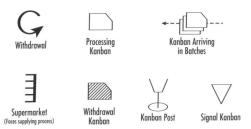

This is how a supermarket pull system works:

- Customers take only what they need when they need it.
- Supplier produces to replenish only what was withdrawn.
- Defective product and incorrect quantities are never sent to the next process.
- Inventories are lowered by reducing the kanban quantity as problems are solved.

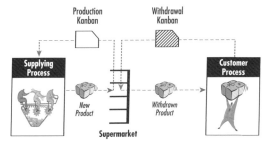

The supermarket should be kept as small as possible to facilitate flow. The supermarket size can be established by considering the usage rate, the refill move quantities, the refill lead time, and the minimum point to signal for more to be produced.

A **FIFO (first in first out) pull system** is used when it's not practical to maintain an inventory of all possible product variations due to having custom products, short shelf life products, or expensive and infrequently ordered products. The icon for a FIFO pull system is:

This is how a FIFO pull system works:
- Products are made-to-order while overall inventory is minimized.
- The first product to enter the FIFO system is also the first one to exit.
- Removal of one unit triggers the supplying process to produce more.
- The system is often maintained with a lane or other visible method.

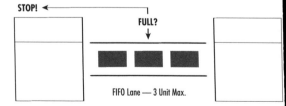

FIFO Lane — 3 Unit Max.

Question 4 Example
In the example Future State Value Stream map, we have shown the
Assemble and Pack & Ship processes as one continuous flow
process. This new process pulls from the supermarket, which is
filled by the receive process. We have also targeted using a supermarket pull system for supplier materials and for finished goods.

A SUPERMARKET PULL SYSTEM

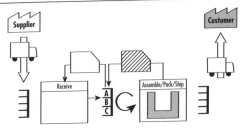

If this Value Stream provided a custom service, FIFO pull systems
might replace supermarkets.

*QUESTION 5: AT WHAT SINGLE POINT (THE PACEMAKER) IN THE
VALUE STREAM IS PRODUCTION TRIGGERED?*
The **pacemaker** is the one point that is scheduled in the Value
Stream. The pacemaker sets the pace for the entire Value Stream.
It is controlled by the pace of customer needs and is NOT the bottleneck, or slowest process! This is not what the Value Stream can
now do, but what is needed to build at the customer's pace. This
is where the drummer sits, using the earlier analogy of drumbeat
to signal Takt time.

The pacemaker should be set as close to the customer as possible. However, service and transactional Value Streams typically require the pacemaker to be placed further upstream in the process.

Question 5 Example
In the example Value Stream, the new assemble/pack/ship cell can set the pace for the Value Stream. We have used a drum icon to indicate the pacemaker on the VSM.

QUESTION 6: HOW IS PRODUCTION MIX LEVELED AT THE PACEMAKER?
Production mix refers to the different varieties or types of products. The Lean principle is: make every product every day. The goal is to have a flexible and responsive Value Stream that can produce any variety that the customer needs. A supermarket pull system can facilitate leveling the mix, since it makes the variety of products visible and easier to manage.

And, as batch sizes are reduced and we get closer to one-at-a-time, our ability to make a particular product variety as the customer needs it increases. The Future State Value Stream mapping icon is:

Question 6 Example
In the example Value Stream, we should make some A's, B's, and C's each day versus making A's on Monday, B's on Tuesday, and C's on Wednesday, etc. This is how we might show this in the Future State Value Stream map:

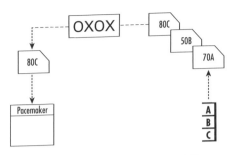

QUESTION 7: HOW IS PRODUCTION VOLUME LEVELED AT THE PACEMAKER?

Production **volume** is leveled at the pacemaker by producing to Takt time. Visual feedback is needed to determine how each process is performing to Takt time. In a custom order, service, or transactional Value Stream, each unit may take a different amount of **work content**. One option in this case is to set the demand calculation as a time increment of product instead of a unit. Then, different variations can be defined as certain time increments for the purpose of managing flow to Takt time.

However, if the Takt time is seconds or only a few minutes, feedback may come at such a fast pace that it's meaningless.

To establish a reasonable management/feedback timeframe, Lean uses a multiple of Takt time, or **pitch**. Pitch is often calculated using **pack-out quantity**, or **pack size** of finished goods. This is the amount of product removed for the customer at once. This could be a pallet of widgets, an order of laundry, or a batch run of transactions.

Pitch should be a reasonable time set to
- schedule and handle materials.
- monitor production.
- respond to problems.

Question 7 Example
In the example Value Stream, let's assume that the average order size is 5 units. In this case, 20 minutes seems to be a reasonable timeframe to receive feedback on adherence to Takt time.

Pitch = Takt time (4 min.) x 5 = 20 min.

QUESTION 8: WHAT PROCESS IMPROVEMENTS ARE NECESSARY FOR THE FUTURE STATE TO BECOME A REALITY?
To make the Future State Value Stream map a reality, improvements in certain areas are required. Key improvements required are noted on the Value Stream map as Kaizen bursts. **Kaizen** is a Japanese term for continuous improvement. The icon for a Kaizen burst is:

Question 8 Example
The example Future State Value Stream will require reducing processing times by eliminating waste as well as cross training so people can help out with different tasks. Other common improvements can include setup reduction, moving people and/or processes closer together, etc. The following is one version of a completed Future State Value Stream map. Note that the total lead time has been reduced from 763.5 minutes to 106 minutes!

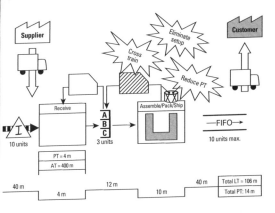

SELECTING THE RIGHT PROJECT TO BEGIN MAKING THE LEAN VALUE STREAM A REALITY

The Future State Value Stream map represents a new design for an entire Value Stream. In most cases, this is too much change for one effort, team, or project. It is better to create projects that are manageable within this overall design and that can be completed in no more than six months. These are called **project "loops"** because we draw loops around different parts of the Future State Value Stream map.

The next steps are:

1. Identify project "loops" on the Future State Value Stream map.

2. Prioritize those projects.

3. Determine the timeframe for each project and the sequence for implementation.

4. Complete project charter/s, assign team/s and get going.

It may be possible to work on the different project "loops" simultaneously by coordinating different teams and efforts. Or, it may be necessary to work on one loop at a time.

CONTINUOUS FLOW CELLS

Since continuous flow is a primary goal of Lean, let's further define a continuous flow cell before identifying the project "loops."

A **cell** is an arrangement of people, machines, material, and methods with the processing steps placed right next to each other in sequential order, through which parts are processed one-at-a-time in a continuous flow. We get as close to one-at-a-time as possible — this may be a small batch that is consistently maintained through the sequence of processing steps. An example of an office cell is shown below.

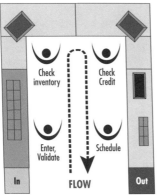

- Multifunctional
- Co-located
- One-at-a-time flow
- Standardized work
- WIP can be held constant
- Flexible work assignments
- Easy communications
- More efficient use of space
- Unbalanced operations are visible, allowing for corrective action

STEP 1: IDENTIFYING THE PROJECT "LOOPS"

Identifying the project "loops" requires an understanding of the Future State design and the work that will be required to make it a reality. We have identified possible project "loops" for the example Value Stream below.

Note that four projects have been identified, each requiring certain knowledge, skills, and effort.

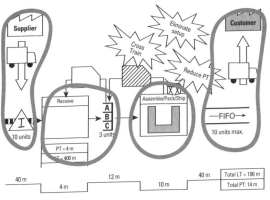

STEP 2: PRIORITIZING THE PROJECT "LOOPS"

There is no hard and fast rule for prioritizing the project "loops"; however, the following guidelines are recommended:

- Begin as close to the customer as possible to begin the pull from the customer and make improvements visible to the customer sooner.

- Focus on the pacemaker process, or cell, since this will set the pace to Takt time for the entire Value Stream.

- Work on the processes within your control before branching out to suppliers or customers; your internal work may change requirements.

- Learn as you go and apply what you learn; don't be afraid to revise the Future State design as you learn more.

- And, finally, ask the question: "Which loop has the best chance of making the greatest improvement considering the customer and the business?"

STEP 3: DETERMINING THE TIMEFRAMES

A review of the data collected may also uncover the need to collect or analyze additional data to determine project timeframes and sequencing. Key data to consider include

- the Product Family — confirm the products included.

- the product volumes — understand fully all variations and trends, including how product mix is handled.

- the information flows — What is it and how does it get communicated?

- the material flows — What are the materials used (can be information)? Where do they come from? How are they managed?

- the people — Who has what knowledge? Who provides indirect support?

- the physical flow (can be virtual — networks or systems) — review the Spaghetti Diagram, measuring distances and noting problems.

- metrics — How is the Value Stream measured? What measures can be used for the project "loops" identified?

The result of this analysis is an implementation plan. In the example Value Stream, we selected the continuous flow cell —

Assemble/Pack/Ship — as the first project since it is close to the customer and the pacemaker.

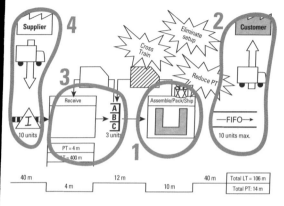

Complete project charters should be done for each project (see Define chapter for details on how to do a project charter). These include scope, timeframes, problem statements, goals, and measures. Team members for each project should be carefully chosen given the data from Step 3. We highly recommend that there be some common team members for all projects within a Value Stream to ensure that the overall Future State design is implemented successfully.

ANALYZING TIME AND WORK

A core principle of Lean is to be synchronized with the customer. Takt time is the available time divided by customer demand. We want to build to Takt time in an even, balanced flow. Therefore, the work must be designed to cycle within Takt. In order to design the work, we need to analyze the work being done in the chosen project "loop."

TAKT TIME AND DAILY DEMAND VARIATION

Most Value Streams do not have a constant customer demand. If you are making widgets and have low daily variation in demand, it is possible to operate at a constant Takt time and meet demand with occasional overtime or a small finished goods inventory.

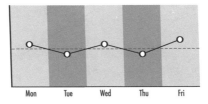

If you are making widgets and have a high daily variation in demand, it is possible to operate at a constant Takt time and meet demand with a larger finished goods inventory.

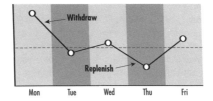

However, if your product is a custom widget, a service, or a transaction, the daily demand can have high variation, but inventory cannot be used to buffer this variation. The options include varying available time or using a different Takt time each day.

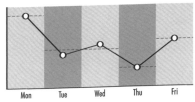

Another consideration is leveling the mix, or how to build every product variation every day. **Interval** is the elapsed time it takes to cycle through all products in the product family.

Batch Production

Run a large batch of Product A, then change to Product B, then to Product C. After all products are run, start over with Product A.

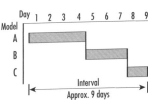

ANALYZING THE WORK

The next step is to analyze the work within the selected project "loop." **Work element** is the smallest increment of work that can be transferred from one person to another. The work content is the sum of all work elements to make one unit start to finish within the project scope of the Value Stream. You will most likely be analyzing the work for one project "loop" at a time.

Breaking processes into work elements helps identify and eliminate waste and readjust workloads. In order to do this analysis we must:

1. Identify the work elements.
2. Time each element.

In identifying work elements, we will find **in-cycle work**, or the normal repetitive work elements required to perform the job; and **out-of-cycle work**, or activities that do not occur every cycle. Examples of out-of-cycle work include replenishing supplies, getting tools, or stopping to check the schedule.

We will NOT include out-of-cycle work in the new cell. We will eliminate it, convert it to in-cycle work, or assign it outside the cell.

DETERMINING WORK ELEMENTS
1. Define the scope of work to analyze.
2. Observe a qualified person to get a sense of the overall job.
3. Observe several cycles, define each element and refine.
4. Describe each element with a clear beginning and end.
5. Record elements in the sequence they are done.
6. Separate people and equipment activities.
7. Identify and record out-of-cycle work.

TIMING WORK ELEMENTS
Collect real times at the process using a qualified person (not necessarily the slowest or fastest) for each separate work element as defined above. Select the lowest repeatable time (**mode**), the average, or the **median** time (middle number). Choose which is most representative of the work element over time. Below is a process study form for one work element in the process Assemble:

Process	Work Element	1	2	3	4	Lowest Repeatable	Notes
Assemble	Attach Part A to Part B	.4	.5	.5	.5	.5	

IMPROVING WORK ELEMENTS

To begin analyzing and improving the work elements in the project "loop," create a **single stack** of all work elements required to make one unit. A single stack is a "stack," or list, of all work elements with the time for each. See the example on the next page — a bar chart is frequently used to depict a single stack.

Next, create a **paper kaizen** for these work elements. This is a list of all work elements with improvements possible given the plan to create a continuous flow cell. Guidelines for creating a paper kaizen include:

- Do not include walking time.
- Do not include out-of-cycle work.
- If possible, convert out-of-cycle to in-cycle work.
- Do not include time waiting for equipment — we will assume that people can do other tasks while equipment is working.
- Do not include unload time if automated ejection could reasonably be used.

See the following single stack and paper kaizen examples. Note that the improvements shown are made by combining the two processes into one continuous flow cell as designed in the example Future State Value Stream map. We have not rearranged any work elements yet! Nor, have we thought about distributing work elements to people.

SINGLE STACK AND PAPER KAIZEN EXAMPLE

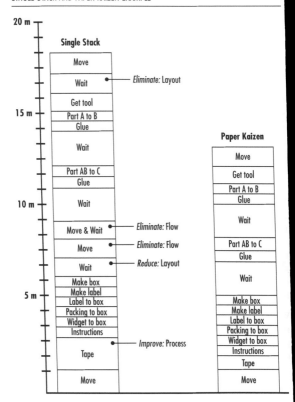

ANALYZING EQUIPMENT EFFECTIVENESS

Almost all Value Streams have some equipment. It may be heavy automatic equipment in a manufacturing process, light equipment manually operated, or a combination of computers, networks, and printers in an office. So, ALL Lean implementations should include analyzing equipment as yet another factor in eliminating waste and increasing flow.

COLLECTING EQUIPMENT DATA

Since all processes must have the capability to cycle within Takt time, the cycle time of equipment is key. **Machine cycle** is the time required to produce one unit; it does not include load, start, and unload. Typically we use the machine cycle plus load and unload to test the capability to cycle within Takt, IF we are assuming that setup time is accounted for in extra inventory.

Effective machine cycle is the machine cycle + load/start/unload time + (setup time ÷ **batch size**). We use this measure to test the capability to cycle within Takt time when we are not assuming that setup time is accounted for in extra inventory. This decision should be based on how the future process will really run. Note in the following example that machine 1 has the capability to cycle much faster than Takt. We do not want to do this since this would result in overproduction!

When the capability to cycle exceeds Takt time, we have a **bottleneck**. Bottleneck refers to any condition where the cycle time of a process (automated or not) exceeds Takt time. In the following example, machine 3 is a bottleneck.

EQUIPMENT CYCLE VS. TAKT TIME

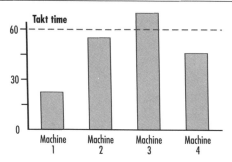

The defect rate is the total number of defects produced ÷ the total number of units produced. Again, this applies to any process.

Uptime is (scheduled hours – unplanned downtime) ÷ scheduled hours. This measure is usually associated with equipment and identifies the time that the machine/process really ran compared to the time planned to run. Scheduled hours would typically be available time – planned downtime.

STEPS TO COLLECT EQUIPMENT DATA
Below are the steps to begin collecting data to analyze each piece of equipment within the cell:

1. Collect basic data as explained above.
2. Determine if each has
   a. a long setup time.
   b. chronic quality problems.
   c. excessive unplanned downtime.
3. Calculate machine cycle and/or effective machine cycle.

---

4. Evaluate the capability to cycle vs. Takt time.

5. Identify approach for any bottleneck conditions.

6. Determine whether needed equipment can be dedicated to the cell.

What If a Bottleneck Is Identified?

If bottlenecks are found, there are several things that can be done to reduce the effective machine cycle:

- Reduce setup times.
- Improve load/start/unload times.
- Reduce the machine cycle.
- Move some of the work to another machine, or use two machines.
- Duplicate the cell or decouple the machine from the cell and use pull.
- Increase the available time and, therefore, the Takt time.

GUIDELINES FOR EQUIPMENT IN THE CELL

- Plan the effective machine cycle to be no more than 80% of Takt time.
- Avoid complex, large, multi-functional equipment resulting in higher cost per increment, less flexibility, and often less reliability.
- Use simple, small, single-function machines which are less costly, more flexible, and have shorter cycle times.
- Make setup time support an interval of one day or less (to support making every part every day) and less than one Takt time cycle at the pacemaker.
- Avoid and/or reduce batching.
- Design in maintainability.

WHEN TO AUTOMATE

Note the following diagram, which explains the levels of automation. The first thing to automate (in level 2) is the machine cycle itself. The second thing to consider automating is the unload process (level 3). There is a "great divide" between levels 3 and 4 in terms of technology required and cost to automate.

	Load Machine	Machine Cycle	Unload Machine	Transfer Part
1	Manual	Manual	Manual	Manual
2	Manual	Auto	Manual	Manual
3	Manual	Auto	Auto	Manual

"The Divide"

	Load Machine	Machine Cycle	Unload Machine	Transfer Part
4	Auto	Auto	Auto	Manual
5	Auto	Auto	Auto	Auto

Automation guidelines include:

- Introduce auto-eject whenever operators must use both hands to handle a part.
- Install one-touch automation where possible.
- Incorporate sensors to signal abnormal conditions and stop machines if necessary, so operators don't need to watch machines during their cycle.

OVERALL EQUIPMENT EFFECTIVENESS

Measuring and analyzing equipment effectiveness reflects how well equipment is being utilized. This can help us improve productivity, flow, and quality by identifying key areas of improvement. Our goal in Lean is to balance equipment effectiveness with adherence to Takt time!

Overall Equipment Effectiveness (OEE) is a way to measure equipment based on the six losses (or wastes associated with equipment):

Downtime Losses (Availability)
1. Equipment failure (breakdowns)
2. Setup and adjustment

Efficiency Losses (Production Efficiency)
3. Minor stoppages
4. Reduced speed

Quality Losses (Quality Rate)
5. Defects
6. Reduced yield

OEE = AVAILABILITY x EFFICIENCY x QUALITY

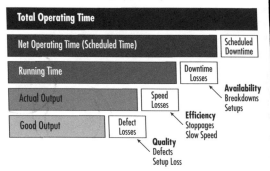

Total operating time = 24 hours, 7 days a week

Net operating time = total operating time − scheduled downtime

Running time = Net operating time − downtime losses due to breakdowns and setups

Actual output = Running time − speed losses due to stoppages and slow speed

Good output = Actual output − defect losses due to any defects and setup losses (product destroyed while setting up)

The goal for Lean is that equipment can produce good parts during at least 85 percent of scheduled time. As a rule of thumb, aim for at least:

- Availability: > 90 percent
- Efficiency: > 95 percent
- Quality: > 99 percent

TOTAL PRODUCTIVE MAINTENANCE

Total Productive Maintenance (TPM) is a companywide approach for improving the effectiveness, longevity, and uptime of equipment. It was first introduced in the early 1970s and combined preventative maintenance practices, Total Quality Control (TQC), and employee involvement. TPM is critical to Lean because it attacks downtime and quality losses, both important wastes that can have significant negative impact on flow and lead time. TPM also harnesses the efforts of all employees towards quality, safety, and efficiency.

TPM AND LEAN

Reliable equipment is a Lean requirement!

- Lean's short lead times and minimal inventory require reliable processes, so equipment breakdowns and defects must be minimized.

- Waste reduction in fixed assets requires equipment to run at the rate needed, when needed, without producing defective parts.

- Lean projects expose equipment reliability issues; improvements deteriorate if these issues are not addressed.

ANALYZING EQUIPMENT SETUP

Setup is the act of changing from one job or type of job to another. Since effort and time are usually required to make this change, setups tend to be done infrequently, and, therefore, work gets done in large batches. We tend to think of setups in manufacturing Value Streams, but setups also exist in service and transactional Value Streams as a result of machine-related issues (i.e., loading a different software program) or external requirements ("We only do applications on Thursdays").

Other terms often used for setup include changeover and SMED (Single Minute Exchange of Dies). Proven methodologies for reducing setup time exist, but are not detailed here.

WHY REDUCE SETUP TIME?

The following five reasons for reducing setup time are discussed in more detail in subsequent sections.

1. Reduce the interval, improving responsiveness and flexibility.
2. Reduce inventory by reducing batch sizes.
3. Improve quality by standardizing the process and reducing variability.
4. Make the setup easier to do, simplifying steps and fixing problems.
5. Recover capacity, saving time to produce more product.

WHAT IS SETUP REDUCTION?

The idea behind setup reduction is not to "hurry up" to get the setup done faster. It is to simplify the setup, making it easier to do while working at a normal pace.

The setup redesign process consists of the following steps:

1. Analyze the way the setup is currently done.
2. Eliminate what can be done before or after the setup.
3. Fix recurring problems.
4. Simplify what remains.

IDENTIFYING POTENTIAL CAUSES

So far we have been addressing Lean solutions. However, we will not be able to maximize the results in the Future State if there is too much variation or other defects such as rework or scrap. We will need to solve those problems.

Once the problem has been focused, the team will create a list of potential causes and then organize those causes in order to see relationships between cause and effect. An underlying assumption of many of the tools used in the Analyze phase is that the data roughly fit a normal distribution. It might be necessary to transform data that do not fit a normal distribution. Causes are verified so that improvements focus on the deep cause, not on the original symptom.

It is time to generate a lot of potential causes, organize them, and decide which potential causes to verify.

BRAINSTORMING

Often team members believe that they know the root cause of a problem. Perhaps they are right, but maybe they are wrong. In the Analyze phase, the aim is to brainstorm ideas in order to get a large quantity of potential causes. The concern here is quantity, not quality, of ideas; so it is crucial that there be no criticism of ideas. Later, the quality of the ideas can be judged.

Brainstorming Rules:
- Start with silent thinking time.
- Set a time limit.
- Encourage creativity.
- Don't evaluate; suspend criticism.
- Build on ideas.
- Post ideas.
- Consider a round-robin to encourage balanced participation.

THE FIVE WHYS

When the ideas have been chosen, they should be affinitized. (See Affinity Diagrams in the Define Phase.) The next step is to use the **Five Whys** to ask why? for each of the potential causes in order to drive down to a root cause. Here is an example.

Problem: Orders have frequent errors in the dye lot number.
1. Why? Samples often are missing their labels.
2. Why? Labels fall off in humid weather.
3. Why? Glue on labels doesn't meet our needs.
4. Why? We have no written specs for label supplier.
5. Why? No process for writing vendor specs.

Root Cause: There is no defined process for writing specs for labels with the vendor so that the labels will stick through all types of weather.

CAUSE-AND-EFFECT DIAGRAM

Cause-and-Effect Diagrams are also known as **fishbone** or **Ishikawa** diagrams. They
- provide structure for determining cause-and-effect relationships.
- provide a visual representation of relationships between potential causes.
- help prevent jumping to a solution without identifying root causes.

SAMPLE CAUSE-AND-EFFECT DIAGRAM

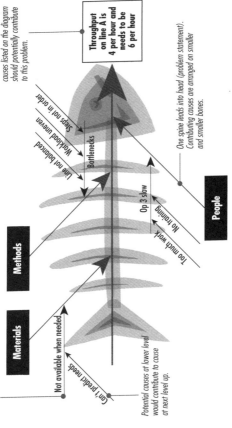

Narrowly defined problem forms the head of the fish; causes listed on the diagram should potentially contribute to this problem.

Throughput on line A is 4 per hour and needs to be 6 per hour

One spine leads into head (problem statement). Contributing causes are arranged on smaller and smaller bones.

People

Steps not in order

Bottlenecks

Workload uneven

Line not balanced

Op 3 slow

No training

Too much work

Methods

Materials

Not available when needed

Arrows indicate the direction of potential cause and effect.

(Can't) predict needs

Potential causes at lower level would contribute to cause at next level up.

How to Construct a Cause-and-Effect Diagram

1. Define the problem, symptom, or effect.

2. Place the problem or symptom at the right, enclosed in a box.

3. Draw the central spine as a thick line pointing to it from the left.

4. Identify possible causes (Brainstorming).

5. Sort possible causes into major categories (Affinity diagram).

6. Connect categories to central spine.

7. Within each category ask, "Why does this condition exist?" (Five Whys)

8. Continue to add causes to each branch.

Using Cause-and-Effect Diagrams

• Place the focused problem statement in the big box. (Example: Throughput on line A is 4 per hour and needs to be 6 per hour.)

• Categorize the causes and put the categories at the end of each bone emanating from the central spine. (Example: Materials, Methods, People)

• Note that the example might not be the same as your categories.

• Place each cause and sub-cause in the categories. (Example: Not available when needed; sub-cause: Can't predict needs)

VERIFYING CAUSES

As previously stated, the cause-and-effect diagram contains the potential causes. It is now time to verify the potential causes with data. The question becomes: "Which causes should we verify?" The answer depends on a number of things. Here are some guidelines:

- Verify causes where data are on hand.
- Verify causes where data are easy to collect.
- Verify causes that the subject matter experts think are the important theories.

Testing a Theory with Data —
A problem with the output of a process (Y) is caused by either Input or Process variables (Xs). Another way to state this is Y is a function of the Xs; or with an equation: $Y = f(X_1, X_2, X_3, X_i)$.

The challenge is to decide which tool to use to demonstrate the relationship between the Xs and Y. This depends on the type of data you collect. The following chart should help.

Analyzing Cause-and-Effect Data
The type of data you have or will collect determines what tools you can use:
- Scatter plots
- Frequency plots
- Tables of results or Pareto

		X Axis (Potential Cause)	
		Continuous	Discrete
Y Axis (Effect)	Continuous	Scatter Plots	Stratified Frequency Plots
	Discrete	Stratified Frequency Plots	Pareto or table

When you are trying to reduce common cause variation, it is possible that all the brainstormed ideas on the cause-and-effect diagram are causing the problem. The aim in the Analyze phase is to identify the vital few causes, that is, the few causes that are creating most of the variation.

In many cases, data analysis is not enough. For example, you might find that increased machine speed is reducing yield. The data can show you that. But what is causing the increased machine speed? This will involve spending time observing the process and looking for such things as different methods by different operators, ambiguities in the SOP, etc. Detailed process maps were covered in the Define phase. Here we want to note that the process map must be verified. Six Sigma practitioners need to spend a good deal of time observing the process — on different days, on different shifts, on different machines, etc.

Value Stream Analysis or Data Analysis
It is recommended to use both Value Stream and data analyses to make sure that potential causes are not overlooked.

Value Stream Analysis — Value Stream Maps, Detailed Process Maps, Value-Added Analysis, Lead Time Analysis (*discussed in Chapter 3, Measure phase*):
- To improve the understanding of process flow
- To tackle lead time problems
- To identify opportunities to reduce process costs

Data Analysis — Stratification, Scatter plots, frequency plots:
- To understand the drivers of variation in the process
- To tackle quality problems and waste
- To understand the root cause of differences between outputs

STRATIFIED FREQUENCY PLOTS

Stratified frequency plots are useful when you have both continuous and discrete data. For example, you might want to stratify loan processing time (continuous Y) by day of week (discrete X).

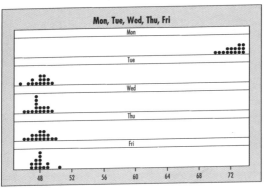

It is clear from the plot that the processing time on Mondays is much longer than on other days. Note that the X scale is the same for each day. This is a case in point where further process analysis is necessary: "Monday" of itself does not cause anything. We need to observe the process on the days of the week to find out what is different about Mondays.

In another example you might be concerned about loan approval on first pass (discrete Y), and the theory is that when we spend enough time with the customer (continuous X), it is more likely that loans will be approved on first pass. Note that the X scale is the same for No and Yes.

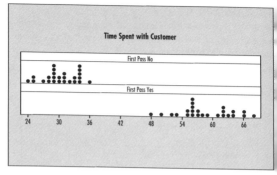

SCATTER PLOTS

When both the X and Y are continuous, or at least numeric, we can use a **scatter plot** to see if there is a correlation between the two variables. The idea is to see if the output (Y) changes as the input or process variable (X) changes.

Creating a Scatter Plot

Suppose we suspected that machine temperature (X) was decreasing the yield (Y) of paint (measured in liters). We would collect data on the yield at different machine temperatures. That is, the data would be paired. A scatter plot would use the minimum and maximum of yield for the Y axis, and the minimum and maximum of speed for the X axis. Then the paired data could be plotted and the graph could be interpreted.

Interpreting a Scatter Plot

In graph 1 you would interpret that there was a strong negative relationship between temperature and yield. That is, as temperature increases, yield decreases. You would interpret graph 2 as a moderate negative relationship. The closer together the data points are, the stronger the relationship. In graph 3, you would interpret that there was no relationship. That is, as temperature increases, yield does not change.

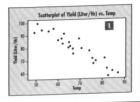

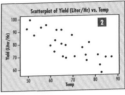

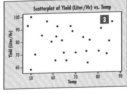

On the other hand, the theory might be that as temperature increases, yield increases. You suspect a positive correlation.

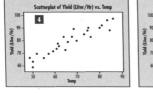

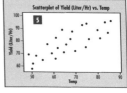

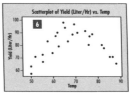

In graph 4, there is a strong positive relationship. That is, as temperature rises, yield rises. In graph 5 the relationship is only moderate. In graph 6 we see a non-linear relationship. That is, as temperature rises, yield rises, but when temperature gets above 70 degrees, yield begins to decrease.

CORRELATION AND CAUSATION

Even strong **correlation** does not imply causation.

- Ice cream sales and the number of shark attacks on swimmers are correlated.
- Skirt lengths and stock prices are highly correlated.
- People with bigger feet are better spellers.

Correlation May Be Due to:

- Causation: Changes in X cause changes in Y.
- Common response: Both X and Y respond to changes in some other variable.

- Ice cream sales and shark attacks both increase during summer.
- Skirt lengths and stock prices both go up in politically liberal climates.
- **Confounding**: The effect of X on Y is mixed up with the effects of other explanatory variables on Y.
  - People with bigger feet are also older and have learned more about the rules of spelling.

VERIFY CAUSE REVIEW

- Select the most likely causes to verify.
- Use existing data or collect new data to see if these causes contribute to the problem.
- Use scatter plots, stratified frequency plots, tables, or experimentation to understand the relationship between causes and effects.

VERIFYING CAUSE USING STATISTICAL TOOLS

Statistical Tools

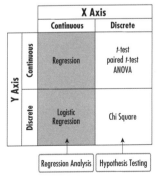

		X Axis	
		Continuous	**Discrete**
Y Axis	**Continuous**	Regression	t-test paired t-test ANOVA
	Discrete	Logistic Regression	Chi Square
		↑	↑
		Regression Analysis	Hypothesis Testing

HYPOTHESIS TESTS

A **hypothesis test** is a procedure that summarizes data so you can detect differences among groups. It is used to make comparisons between two or more groups.

Examples of what you might want to compare	What you want to compare	Data type
Is their a difference in lead time by shift?	Averages	Continuous
Has the improvement reduced the variation?	Variation	Continuous
Does the % of defects differ by day of week?	Proportions	Discrete

HOW HYPOTHESIS TESTS WORK

Null hypothesis: (H_0) there is no difference between groups.
Alternative hypothesis: (H_a) the groups are different.

- There will always be some variation between groups. Hypothesis testing is used to determine whether the differences are due to random, common cause variation.
- The P-value is the probability of obtaining the observed difference given that the null hypothesis is true.
- P-values range from 0.0 to 1.0 (0% chance to 100% chance).
  - $P < .05$ suggests the difference is significant; reject the null hypothesis and accept the alternative hypothesis.

If the P-value is less than 0.05:
- Reject the H_0 and conclude the H_a.
- There is less than a 5% chance that the groups came from the same distribution.
- The observed difference is a statistically significant difference and is unlikely to be caused by common cause (random) variation.

ASSUMPTIONS FOR HYPOTHESIS TESTS

- For continuous data:
  - Normal distribution
  - Non-normal data may need to be transformed.
- For populations:
  - Independent samples
  - Random samples
  - Representative samples
- For processes:
  - Stable processes
  - No special causes or shifts over time
  - Representative samples
- While hypothesis testing was designed to compare populations, it is often used to compare processes, most of which are unstable.
- Hypothesis testing is an advanced topic as it assumes a stable process.

TYPES OF HYPOTHESIS TESTS

Type of Data	What you can compare	Tests
Discrete	Proportions	Test of two proportions Chi Square test
Continuous	Averages	2-Sample *t*-test (two group averages) Paired *t*-test (group averages with matched data) ANOVA (two or more group averages)
	Variation	Test for equal variances Components of variance

HOW TO USE A HYPOTHESIS TEST

1. Determine the type of test suited to your data and question.

2. Select the appropriate test.

3. Obtain p-value; declare statistically significant difference if $p < 0.05$.

TWO TYPES OF ERRORS IN HYPOTHESIS TESTING

There are four possible outcomes to any decision we make based on a hypothesis test. We can decide the groups are the same or different, and we can be right or wrong.

		Truth	
		Groups are Different	Groups are Same
Decision	Reject H_0 Groups are Different	Correct	Type I Error
	Accept H_0 Groups are Same	Type II Error	Correct

Type I error — Deciding the groups are different when they aren't (the difference is due to random variation)

- P-value = the probability of making a Type I error (that is, deciding the groups are different when they really aren't).

- You choose what level of Type I error you are willing to live with; by convention, it is usually set at 0.05 (= 5% chance).

Type II error — Not detecting a difference when there really is one

- The probability of making a Type II error can be calculated given an assumed true difference.

Practical Implications of Type I and Type II Errors
- Both Type I and Type II errors are important.
- Avoiding one type of error increases the risk of the other error.
- Increasing the sample size reduces the risk of Type II errors and allows you to detect smaller differences.

T-TEST

We use a statistical test called the *t*-test for comparing and judging differences between two group averages:

$$t_{(\bar{A} - \bar{B})} = \frac{(\bar{X}_A - \bar{X}_B) - 0}{S_{(\bar{A} - \bar{B})}}$$

THE CONFIDENCE INTERVAL

95% confidence interval: the range of values expected to contain the true difference between two group averages.
- If there is no significant difference, the confidence interval will contain 0; that is, it will range from negative to positive.
- It is based on the difference between averages, not the individual observations.
- The range for individual values would be wider.

T-TEST SUMMARY

The *t*-test compares two averages.
- The null hypothesis is that the two group averages are the same H_0: mean$_A$ = mean$_B$.
- The alternative hypothesis is that the averages are different H_a: mean$_A$ ≠ mean$_B$.

- Calculate the *t*-statistic from the data and provide the P-value.
- If P-value is < .05, reject the null hypothesis and accept the alternative hypothesis with 95% confidence.
- If P is ≥ .05, conclude there is not sufficient evidence to reject the null hypothesis because
    - The groups are the same; or
    - The variation is too large; or
    - the sample is too small to detect a difference.

PAIRED T-TEST
Matched or paired data

In a **paired *t*-test** two measurements are obtained for each sampling unit (a transaction, phone call, employee, deal, application, etc.).

Measurements in the second group are not independent from those in the first group. They are matched or paired. The second measurements are taken on the same sampling units as the first measurements.

Practical implications of Paired *t*-test:
- The paired *t*-test is a powerful way to compare two methods.
- It requires a special matched data structure. The sampling unit (a machine, operation, etc.)
    - has each method applied to it,
    - with little or no carryover from the use of the first method to the use of the second.
    - requires planning.
    - The paired *t*-test applies in the analysis or improvement stages of a project.
    - For example, you're seeking to find or demonstrate a difference between two ways of analyzing a lab test.

SUMMARY: PAIRED T-TEST

Null hypothesis (H_0): There is no difference between the paired groups (average paired difference = 0).

Alternative hypothesis (H_a): The paired groups are different (average paired differences $\neq 0$).
- There is less variation due to differences in the sampling units.
- Fewer samples are needed to find a significant difference between the groups.

ANOVA

Comparing two or more group averages

ANOVA is a statistical test that uses variances to compare multiple averages simultaneously. Instead of comparing pair-wise averages, it compares the variance between groups to the variance within groups.

The between-group variance is obtained from the variance (s^2) of the group averages. The within-group variance is obtained from the variance (s^2) among values within each group, and then pooled (or averaged with appropriate degrees of freedom) across the groups.

If the variance between groups is the same as the variance within groups, we say there is no difference between the group averages.

$$\frac{S^2_{between}}{S^2_{within}}$$

- Obtain the variance between groups.
- Obtain the variance within groups.
- If they are about the same, conclude there is no significant difference between groups.

- The ratio of two variances = F-statistic.
- We get a P-value from the F-distribution.

ASSUMPTIONS FOR ANOVA

- Each group is normally distributed.
- The samples are representative of the population or process.
- The process is stable.
- The variance for each group is the same (verified with the Test for Equal Variances).

DOES THE VARIATION DIFFER BETWEEN GROUPS? HOW TO CHECK

There is a statistical test called Test for Equal Variance (sometimes called Homogeneity of Variance) to check this assumption. Homogeneity means the same, so you're testing if the variances are the same.

ANOVA SUMMARY

Analysis of Variance (ANOVA) compares averages of two or more groups.

- Assumes variances of each group are the same
- Also used to compare variances to check the assumption that variances are the same when comparing averages (Homogeneity of Variance test)

COMPONENTS OF VARIANCE

Components of Variance analysis helps you see patterns of variation in response variable(s) which can be correlated with potential causal variables. The specific tool used is called the ANOVA.

- Which model to use depends on whether the design is nested or crossed.
- Both require an equal number of observations at each combination of your treatment levels.

Nested: Suppose there are two factors that you want to measure, line and operator. If two operators measure one line, and two other operators measure the other line, this design is nested.

Crossed: If the same two operators measure each of the lines, this design is crossed.

A **crossed design** might have been used in Gage R&R, where three operators all measured the same five parts.

WHY USE COMPONENTS OF VARIANCE?

- **Components of Variance** analysis can help you narrow a list of potential causes to a much smaller list suitable for detailed investigation, through designed experiments, for example.

- It helps you funnel down to find potential variables that you may need to study.

- It can be used in the Analyze step to complement process analysis and stratification.

FAMILIES (COMPONENTS OF VARIANCE)

Typical families of variation in a manufacturing environment can be clustered together:

Unit families:

- Within-Unit variation: different measurements or results at different points within the unit or product

- Unit-to-Unit: one unit to the next (within sub-group variation)

- Sub-group to sub-group
- Stream-to-stream: vendor-to-vendor, line-to-line, machine-to-machine, tool-to-tool, operator-to-operator, etc.

MULTI-VARI CHART

There is another graph that you can use to display the components of variance called Multi-Vari. However, this is not a statistical tool and does not provide a P-value.

TEST OF TWO PROPORTIONS

Null hypothesis H_0: The proportions of the two groups are the same.

Alternative hypothesis H_a: One group proportion is different from the other group proportion.

If $P \geq .05$:
- Do not reject the H_0.
- There is not enough evidence to declare a statistically significant difference between the group proportions.

If $P < .05$
- Reject the H_0, conclude the H_a.
- One of the group proportions is significantly different than the others.

CHI SQUARE

This is the hypothesis test used to compare two or more group proportions. It is used when both X and Y are discrete. The counts are summarized in a table known as a contingency table. The Chi-Square measures the difference between the observed and the expected counts when both the X and Y data are discrete.

Discrete Ys
- An attribute is recorded for each unit.
  - For example, accuracy (accurate, not accurate), types of errors (wrong address, name, etc.)
- Number of units with each attribute can be counted.
- Counts are usually summarized in a table (contingency table).

Discrete Xs
Stratifies data into groups ("by" variable)
- "How do results vary by location?"
- For example, location, method, product type

NEXT STEPS:
- Determine which group proportions are different.
- Determine why the group proportions are different.

ASSUMPTIONS FOR THE CHI-SQUARE TEST
- The sample is representative of the population or process.
- The underlying distribution is binomial for discrete data.
- The expected count > 5 for each cell.
- If expected count is < 5, collecting additional data (a bigger sample size) will be needed.

VALUE OF A CHI-SQUARE TEST
- Discrete data are often used to analyze process performance in the service applications.
- Knowing whether differences between two or more groups are significant prevents making changes that will be a waste of time.

- If significant differences between group proportions are identified, it's worthwhile to look for root causes in the groups that are different.

Remember to consider whether a statistically significant difference in proportions is actually important to the business.

REGRESSION ANALYSIS

Regression analysis generates a line that quantifies the relationship between X and Y. The line, or regression equation, is represented as $Y = b_0 + b_1$ where:

b_0 = intercept (where the line crosses Y when X = zero)

b_1 = slope (rose over run, or change in Y per unit increase in X)

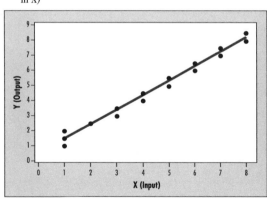

Why quantify the relationship?

- Regression analysis can be used to predict what the value of Y will be with a known value of X.

- If the X being measured can be controlled, it is possible to produce desired outcomes by changing process conditions.

Extrapolation is making predictions outside the range of the X data. It is a natural desire, but it is like walking from solid ground onto thin ice. Predictions from the regression equation are more reliable for Xs within the range of observed data.

A **residual** is the vertical distance from each point to the regression line. It equals Observed Y minus Predicted Y. It is the leftover variation in Y after using X to predict Y.

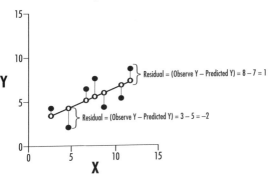

THE LEAST SQUARES METHOD

The **regression equation** is determined by a procedure that minimizes the total squared distance of all points to the line.

- It finds the line where the squared vertical distance from each data point to the line is as small as possible (or the "least").

- Restated…. It minimizes the "square" of all the residuals.

- Regression uses the least squares method to determine the "best line."

- Data (both X and Y values) are used to obtain b_0 and b_1.

- The b_0 and b_1 values establish the equation.

ASSUMPTIONS

Assumptions for regression are based on properties of the residuals (not the original data). We assume residuals are:

- Not related to the Xs: If the relationship between X and Y is not a straight line, but a curve, try a transformation on X, Y, or both, or use curvilinear regression.

- Stable and independent (do not change over time): Any pattern visible over time means another factor, related to time, influences Y. Try to discover it and include it in a multiple regression.

- Constant (do not increase as predicted Ys increase): A fan shape means the variation increases as Y gets larger (it's not constant). Try a square root, log, or inverse transformation on Y.

- Normal distribution: If the residuals are not normal, try a transformation on X or Y or both.

TYPES OF REGRESSION

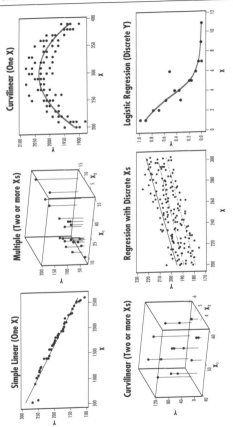

Curvilinear (One X)

Logistic Regression (Discrete Y)

Multiple (Two or more Xs)

Regression with Discrete Xs

Simple Linear (One X)

Curvilinear (Two or more Xs)

CONFIDENCE AND PREDICTION INTERVALS
Confidence Interval
- The confidence interval is an interval likely to contain the "best fit" line.
- It gives a range of the predicted values for the fitted Y if the regression is repeated again,
- based on a given X-value,
- for a given confidence.

Prediction Interval
- The prediction interval is an interval likely to contain the actual Y values for a given X.
- It gives a range of likely actual values for Y,
- based on a given X-value,
- for a given confidence.

REVIEW

Name	Range	Interpretation
B_1 Slope of X_1	$-\infty - \infty$	Unit change in Y for a unit increase in X_1, with all other Xs constant
P-Value of slope Probability the slope is significantly different from 0	$0 - 1$	P < .05 = significant slope X is related to Y.
r Correlation coefficient	$-1 - +1$	The further from 0 (no relationships), the stronger the relationship between X and Y.
R-Sq Explained variation	$0 - 1$	Multiplied by 100, gives the % of variation of the Y values explained by the linear relationship of X and Y.
R-Sq$_{adj}$ R Square adjusted	$0 - <1$	Used to compare models with different numbers of terms
s Standard deviation of the residuals	$0 - \infty$	Shows the unexplained variation, or how much the observed value differs from the fitted value.
Residual Observed Y minus predicted Y	$-\infty - \infty$	Common-cause variation in Y values, assumed to be unrelated to X, random, stable, and normally distributed
Standardized Residuals Residual divided by standard deviation	$\approx -3 - +3$	Standardized residuals $\geq +3$ or ≤ -3 are unusual observations that should be examined.
Influential Observation X value has a large influence on the regression line	$-\infty - \infty$	Plot the points and consider whether or not to use them to calculate the regression line.
VIF Variance Inflation Factor	$1 - \infty$	VIF > 5–10 suggests multi-collinearity. Drop a correlated X and rerun.

DESIGN OF EXPERIMENTS

This is an approach for effectively and efficiently exploring the cause and effect relationship between numerous process variables (Xs) and the output or process performance variable (Y).

- Identifies the "vital few" sources of variation (Xs)
- Quantifies the effects of those vital few Xs, including their interactions
- Quantifies the relationship between the Xs and Y

FULL FACTORIAL

In the Factorial Approach to Designed Experiments

- multiple variables are tested simultaneously.
- Begin by testing two conditions for each variable.
- This approach can test all possible combinations of conditions.
- It uses common cause variation to determine which factors are important through replication of trials.
- It uses methods such as randomization and blocking to deal with factors not controlled in the experiment.

THE FULL FACTORIAL LAYOUT

	Standard Order	Factor 1	Factor 2	Factor 3
	1	–	–	–
	2	+	–	–
	3	–	+	–
	4	+	+	–
	5	–	–	+
	6	+	–	+
	7	–	+	+
	8	+	+	+

Number of Levels (Settings)   Number of Factors

2^3 Full Factorial Design Matrix

A full factorial involves all possible combinations (later we'll look at "fractional factorials" that involve a subset of all runs). For 3 factors, each at 2 levels, there are 2 x 2 x 2 = 8 combinations of factor settings.

2 x 2 x 2 is often written as 2^3. The superscript 3 indicates the number of 2s multiplied together.

In the above diagram you can see the pattern of factor settings in standard order by looking down the columns.

Designing a Full Factorial Experiment
Replication means repeating all the experimental conditions two or more times.

Why Do Replicates?
- To measure common cause variation, the amount of variability among runs performed under the same experimental conditions
- To highlight whether a factor is important
- To examine whether changing factor conditions has an effect on response variability as well as average response by analyzing both the mean and the standard deviation

RANDOMIZATION
Definition:
- To assign the order in which the experimental trials will be run using a random mechanism
- It is not the standard order.
- It is not running trials in an order that is convenient.
- To create a random order, you can "pull numbers from a hat" or have a computer randomize the sequence of trials for you.

Why Randomize?
Randomization of the order of trials averages the effect of any
lurking variables over all of the factors in the experiment and prevents their effects from being mistakenly attributed to some other
factor.

ANALYZING THE EXPERIMENT

- Identify any problems with the data or model.
    - Time series plots of the responses
    - Residual plots
- Identify large effects.
    - Pareto charts
    - Normal probability plots
    - p-values
- Identify effects on responses.
    - Main effects plots
    - Interaction plots
    - Cube plots

RESIDUALS

Definition: Residual = Observed Y − Average of Ys at that experimental condition

- A residual is the difference between a response and what we
  expect it to be (the expected value is the average of all replicates for a particular combination of factor settings).
- We hope most variation in the Ys is accounted for by deliber-
  ate changes we're making in the factor settings.
- Whatever variation is left over is residual.
- The assumption is that this residual variation reflects the
  common cause variation in the experiment.

We assume the residuals are:
- Normal — bell-shaped with a mean of 0
- Constant — do not increase as averages of each experimental condition increase
- Stable — do not change over time
- Not related to the Xs (factors)
- Random — represent common causes of variation
- Independent

Residual plots must be checked to ensure the assumptions hold. Otherwise, conclusions may be incorrect or misleading.

Once you have verified that there are no problems with the data, you can look for factors that have the largest effects on the response. There are two types of effects, main effects and inter-action effects.

RESIDUAL PLOTS

Check to see
that residuals
are randomly
distributed

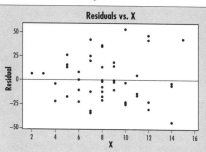

Try a
transformation
on one or both
variables

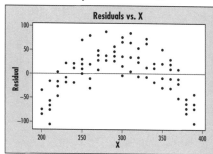

RESIDUAL PLOTS

Assumption Holds

Check to see that residuals are randomly distributed

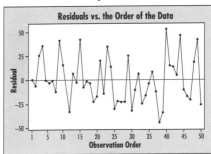

Assumption Does Not Hold

Pattern related to time suggests another factor influencing Y, which should be identified and included in a multiple regression

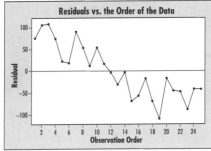

RESIDUAL PLOTS

Assumption Holds

Check to see that residuals are constant over range of Ys

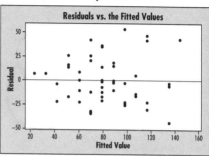

Assumption Does Not Hold

Try a log, square root, or inverse transformation

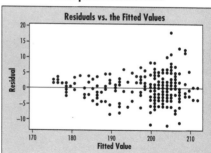

RESIDUAL PLOTS

Assumption Holds

Check to see
that residuals
form a normal
distribution

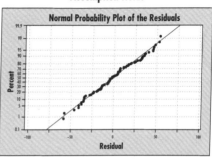

Assumption Does Not Hold

Try a
transformation
on one or both
variables

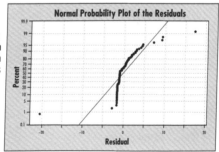

THE MAIN EFFECT

The **main effect** is the average increase (or decrease) in the response when moving from the low to the high level of a factor.

FORMULA FOR CALCULATING MAIN EFFECTS FOR EACH FACTOR

$$\text{MAIN EFFECT} = \begin{pmatrix} \text{Average of all} \\ \text{observations at} \\ \text{High (+) level} \end{pmatrix} - \begin{pmatrix} \text{Average of all} \\ \text{observations at} \\ \text{Low (−) level} \end{pmatrix}$$

INTERACTION EFFECTS

The **interaction effect** is the effect one factor has on the response of another factor, which varies with different levels of the other factor.

$$\text{AB Interaction} = \frac{(\text{Effect of A for high}B) - (\text{Effect of A for low}B)}{2}$$

CALCULATING THE SIZE OF INTERACTION EFFECTS

Deciding Which Effects Are Large (Significant)

There are three ways to decide which effects are large:

- P-value for each effect
- Pareto chart of effects
- Normal probability plot of effects

Drawing Conclusions

- List all your conclusions.
- Interpret the meaning of these results. (For example, relate them to known physical properties, engineering theories, or your own process knowledge.)

- Make recommendations.
- Formulate and write conclusions in simple language.

THE PREDICTION EQUATION — USING COEFFICIENTS

The **prediction equation** quantifies the relationship between the factors and Y.

- Is similar to the regression equation
- Can be used to make predictions of various combinations

For just one numerical factor, suppose the coefficient is 0.25. The prediction equation is Y = Constant + 0.25A.

Dropping Terms from the Prediction Equation

Remove the insignificant terms. If an interaction is significant, it is standard practice to include the main effects of the factors involved, even if the main effects by themselves aren't significant.

Verify Results

- Run a few additional trials at the recommended settings to see if the desired response is achieved.

OR

- Change the process and monitor using a control chart to confirm the desired response is achieved and maintained.

REDUCING EXPERIMENTAL TRIALS — THE HALF-FRACTION AND CONFOUNDING

- In a full factorial design, information is available for all main effects (e.g., A, B, C).
- Interactions:
  - Two-factor (e.g., AB, AC, BC)
  - Higher-order interactions for three or more factors (e.g., ABC, ABCDE)

- When there are many factors, the number of higher-order interactions increases quickly.
- Higher-order interactions are usually negligible (involving more than 2 factors).
- There is a diminishing return of information on higher-order interactions; in general, the higher order they are, the more negligible.

Pros and Cons of a Half-fraction for 5 factors
Pro —
- It halves the number of runs, from 32 to 16 in a five-factor design.

Con —
- Main effects and two-factor interactions are confounded with higher order interactions.

Choosing the Right Design
The knowledge line is a strategy for choosing the appropriate design.

Knowledge of Process

	Screening	Fractional Factorial	Factorial	Response Surface
# Factors	>4	3 – 15	1 – 7	<8
Identifies:	Vital few factors	2-factor interactions	All factor interactions	Optimal factor settings

Which approach to designed experiments you choose depends on how much you already know about a process and how many factors you want to test.

Resolution: Understanding the degree of confounding in a fractional factorial

RESOLUTION	DEGREE OF CONFOUNDING		TYPE OF CONFOUNDING
III	Main effects +	2-factor interactions	Main effects not confounded with each other, but are confounded with 2-factor interactions
	1 + 2 = 3		
IV	Main effects +	3-factor interactions	Main effects not confounded with each other or with 2-factor interactions, but interactions confounded
	1 + 3 = 4 *OR*		
	2-factor Interactions +	other 2-factor interactions	
	2 + 2 = 4		
V	Main effects +	4-factor interactions	Main effects and 2-factor interactions not confounded with each other or 3-factor interactions, but 3-factor interactions counfounded
	1 + 4 = 5 *OR*		
	2-factor Interactions +	2-factor interactions + 3-factor interactions	
	2 + 3 = 5		

The "con" of running fractional factorials is that effects and inter-actions will be confounded.

- The resolution (indicated by the Roman numeral) describes the degree of confounding; the higher the number, the more resolution (= less confounding).
  - A resolution V design has less confounding than a resolution III.
- Resolution tells us the type of effects that will be confounded.

SCREENING DESIGNS

- Study main effects of a large number of factors
- Use roughly the same number of runs as factors
- Resolution III
- Are useful in the early stages of investigation to reduce a large list of factors that might affect the response to a small list of factors that do affect the response

Tips for the analysis of screening designs:
- Check confounding results.
  - An important effect labeled C could also be the result of one or more 2-factor interactions.
- Analyze the collapsed design.
  - If only some factors turn out to be important, drop the other factors and analyze the design again.

PLACKETT-BURMAN DESIGNS

- Create a special pattern of confounding that reduces the number of runs needed.
- Plackett-Burman designs have multiples of 4 runs.
- The main effect is confounded to some degree with every 2-factor interaction, making it more difficult to interpret.

	Runs											
Factorial Screening Designs	4	8		16				32				
Plackett-Burman Designs			12		20	24	28		36	40	44	48

Choosing Plackett-Burman Designs
- Plackett-Burman designs are useful when a large number of factors makes the 2^k (8-, 16-, or 32-run) screening design too costly.
- Do not choose these designs in other circumstances since information about where the 2-factor interactions are confounded is lost.

SUMMARY OF FRACTIONAL FACTORIALS AND SCREENING DESIGNS

- A fractional factorial provides much of the information obtained in a full factorial.
- Screening designs are used to screen a large number of factors to determine which are important.
- Screening designs are Resolution = III (main effects are confounded with 2-factor interactions).
- Resolution tells us which effects are confounded.
- Other fractional factorials can be used to understand which factors and interactions affect the response.
- Plackett-Burman designs can be used when 16 or 32 runs are too costly.

FULL FACTORIALS WITH MORE THAN TWO LEVELS

Full Factorial Designs can be constructed for any number of factors with any number of levels. When there are more than two levels, they provide all the benefits of the Factorial designs, as well as the Response Surface Designs.

Full Factorial Designs often have many runs. For example, a design with
- 1 factor at 2 levels
- 1 factor at 3 levels
- 1 factor at 5 levels

has 30 runs (2 x 3 x 5 = 30).

The design is particularly useful when you want to study a factor that is difficult to represent with two levels. For example, if there are multiple speed settings for a machine, you might want to understand the behavior of all of them, not just two of them.

PLANNING AND PREPARING FOR A DESIGNED EXPERIMENT
Before the Experiment —
- Preliminaries
- Identifying responses, factors, and factor levels
- Selecting the design

During the Experiment —
- Collecting the data

After the Experiment —
- Analyzing the data
- Drawing, verifying, and reporting conclusions
- Implementing recommendations

ANALYZE COMPLETION CHECKLIST
By the end of Analyze, you should be able to
- Design a future state value stream map.
- Identify potential root causes.

- Develop a cause-and-effect diagram.
- Verify relationships using hypothesis testing.
- Quantify relationships between variables using regression analysis and/or designed experiments.
- Begin creating flow with cell design.

ANALYZE PHASE OUTPUTS

- Data analyzed and displayed for easy understanding
- Future state value stream map with loops identified or visual display of the detailed process flow "as is"
- Analysis of process that includes value-added vs. non value-added, bottlenecks, and disconnects
- Identification and verification of root causes
- Sharpened problem statement reflecting the insights gained from applying Lean Six Sigma tools
- An updated stakeholder plan

CONCLUSION

When the team has completed the Analyze Phase, it has a Future State Map and has selected the loop to work on for its project. It has analyzed the process in detail and has identified root causes of problems with hard data. The charter has been finalized, and the team is ready to move to the Improve Phase.

Chapter 5: Improve

In the Improve Phase, you should now be ready to develop, implement, and evaluate solutions targeted at your verified cause. The goal is to demonstrate, with data, that your solutions solve the problem and lead to improvement. The improvement path might require Lean tools, Six Sigma tools, or both. This will depend on the focus of the project along with what was found in the Analyze phase. Recall that customers are concerned about cost, quality,

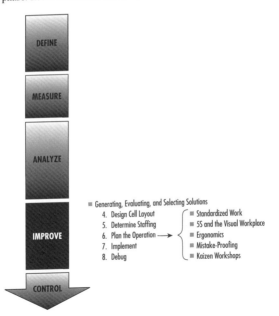

DEFINE

MEASURE

ANALYZE

IMPROVE

CONTROL

■ Generating, Evaluating, and Selecting Solutions
4. Design Cell Layout
5. Determine Staffing
6. Plan the Operation ⟶
7. Implement
8. Debug

■ Standardized Work
■ 5S and the Visual Workplace
■ Ergonomics
■ Mistake-Proofing
■ Kaizen Workshops

and time. If your project was focused on only one of these areas, there will need to be follow-on projects to address all concerns.

The tools most commonly used in the Improve phase are:

1. Brainstorming (*covered in the Analyze phase*)
2. Consensus
3. Cell Design
   a. Design cell layout
   b. Determine staffing
   c. Plan the operation
      i. Standardization
      ii. 5S and Visual Workplace
      iii. Ergonomics
      iv. Mistake-Proofing
      v. Kaizen Workshops
   d. Implement
   e. Debug
4. Creativity techniques
5. Data Collection (*covered in the Measure phase*)
6. Design of Experiments (*covered in the Analyze phase*)
7. FMEA (*covered in the Measure phase*)
8. Hypothesis Tests (*covered in the Analyze phase*)
9. Planning Tools
10. Value Stream and Process Maps (*covered in the Define phase*)
11. Stakeholder Analysis (*covered in the Define phase*)

GENERATING SOLUTIONS

- Review what you know about root causes.
- Brainstorm ideas for solutions.
- Encourage creativity.

EVALUATE IDEAS

In order to achieve better solutions, follow these steps:

- Generate criteria.
- Weight criteria.
- Evaluate ideas.

SOLUTIONS PRIORITIZATION MATRIX

	Criteria				
	Safe	**Low Cost to Implement**	**Little Resistance from Staff**	**Low in Complexity**	**SUM**
Weights	1.65	1.25	1.05	1.05	
Solution					
1	11.55	16.25	9.45	11.55	48.80
2	29.70	20.00	17.85	13.65	81.20
3	24.75	16.25	12.60	15.75	69.35
4	19.80	10.00	12.60	11.55	53.95

Sum of weight times rank   Highest score = winner

COST/BENEFIT ANALYSIS

- At this stage, the team has invested a lot of emotional energy into the project, but the merits of their solution may not be obvious to those outside the team.
- The team might have selected a solution that does not meet the requirements of the business.
- A formal cost/benefit analysis expresses in financial terms the implications of your solution and helps to mobilize commitment and create buy-in.

SELECTING SOLUTIONS

If there is an obvious winner from the evaluation step, go with that choice. If there is no clear choice, use decision making.

Common decision-making techniques:
- Unilateral: One person makes the decision, acting alone.
- Consultative: One person makes the decision after consulting with others.
- Group: The entire team makes the decision together.

Use this checklist to help you decide.
Unilateral
- The decision needs to be made very quickly.
- The person doing the deciding can handle the situations' complexity.
- There is a low need for buy-in by others.

Consultative
- There is enough time to consult with others.
- The situation is complex enough to require input from another person(s).
- Others need to buy into the decision.

Group
- There is enough time to get everyone's perspective.
- The situation is complex enough to require input from the entire team.
- The entire team needs to buy into the decision.

CONSENSUS GUIDELINES

When:

- YES: Setting project goals...selecting a process improvement solution...picking a time for the team to meet
- NO: Determining whether to use a *t*-test to analyze process data... deciding which production lines' data to collect... selecting how/where to print the project documentation report

How:

- Don't just sell your idea...ask questions.
- Seek ways to address the concerns of all...look for "win/win."
- Search for core issues: What's important to the others on the team?
- Listen with an open mind.
- Try arguing the other side to ensure you really understand it.
- Don't allow any member to dominate.
- Hold out for more discussion if you don't agree.

CREATING A CELL LAYOUT FOR ULTIMATE FLOW

We have calculated Takt time, analyzed the work, analyzed equipment within the selected project "loop," and defined and improved work elements. We are now ready to begin designing the continuous flow cell layout.

Note once again that the cell will be designed for ultimate product flow. Designing what the people and/or equipment do in the cell will follow a completed detailed cell layout.

We will do this in three steps:

1. Develop a concept layout.
2. Develop a materials plan.
3. Develop a detailed layout.

STEP 1: DEVELOP A CONCEPT LAYOUT

The final step in improving the work content will be to develop an **ideal sequence** for the work elements. We improved the single stack by doing a paper kaizen in Analyze.

Developing an Ideal Sequence of Work Elements
Now, the order in which the work elements are done is analyzed for improvement. As work elements are re-sequenced, we inevitably will find additional improvements to be included in the ideal sequence. We then use this ideal sequence of work elements to begin designing the cell layout concept.

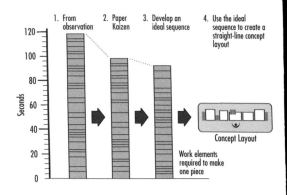

Ideal Sequence Example

Opportunities were found for re-sequencing in the assemble/pack/ship example paper kaizen. The chart below reflects the idea of doing both assemblies before gluing them at the same time and, therefore, having to wait only one time for the glue to set. We also eliminated time from "get tool" with the assumption that an improved layout will make the tool easier to retrieve.

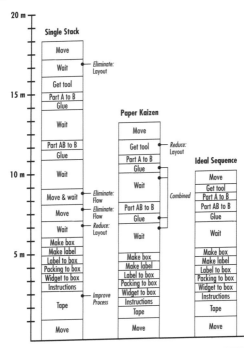

Steps to Develop a Concept Layout

The **concept layout** is developed by following these steps:

1. Start with your ideal sequence of work elements.

2. Make a straight-line concept layout to ensure unidirectional flow.

3. Design for "one operator processing one piece" to ensure that the product flow is good.

4. Determine how parts will be presented to the operator.

5. Traditionally, subassemblies are produced independently of the cell, building in batches and inventory:

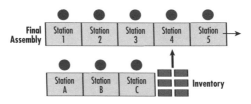

Instead, we want to integrate off-line subassemblies so they produce at the same rate and mix as the cell:

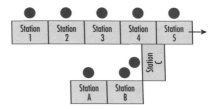

6. Walk through each work element and motion.
7. Apply Motion Economy and Ergonomic principles (see the following for more information).
   a. Reduce the number of motions.
   b. Perform motions simultaneously.
   c. Reduce the distance of each motion.
   d. Make motions easier.
8. Use the walk through to refine the work sequence.

Concept Layout Example
Below is a concept layout for the example cell:

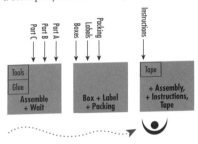

STEP 2: DEVELOP A MATERIALS PLAN
A materials plan should answer the following questions:
- What parts/supplies are involved?
- How will they be handled (racks, containers, etc.)?
- How will they be replenished?
- How much WIP should we plan in the cell?
- What will happen to the empty containers?

Using an Assembly Chart to Clarify the Work

An assembly chart is a very useful way to create a picture of the way that the cell will use the materials required. It shows what parts are involved, where they are used, the order in which they have to be used, and possibly where we have options to make changes.

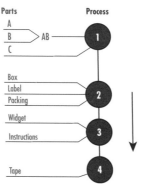

How to Develop a Plan for Every Part

A **plan for every part (PFEP)** can then be developed showing all relevant data, such as usage per day, quantity and size of containers, and how much we need at the cell at one time (or, how often we need replenishment). The following is an example of a PFEP.

A PLAN FOR EVERY PART

Part #	Description	Use/Day	Standard Container					No. of Cards
			Qty.	L	W	H	Wgt.	
3482	A	100	50	15"	10"	6"	5#	4
6593	B	100	50	12"	9"	4"	12#	3
4518	C	100	200	48"	9"	9"	15#	6

Material Handling Checklist

Guidelines for handling materials include:

- Materials should be close to where they will be used, giving operators an opportunity to use both hands simultaneously to retrieve them.
- Replenishment of materials should be done with kanban without interrupting the people doing the work.
- Containers for materials should be designed to help the people using them, not the material handlers or suppliers.
- Work-in-process inventory should be limited to a minimum manageable quantity, and extra inventory should not be stored in or near the cell so that people are tempted to stop to get more material.

Completing the Materials Plan
And finally, develop a complete materials analysis and plan that is clear and easy to follow. The plan should address how, where, and who will manage materials in the cell. And, once again, pictures are better than words!

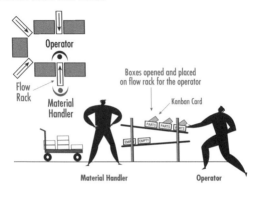

STEP 3: DEVELOP A DETAILED LAYOUT

The concept layout is converted to scale, and equipment is configured to the desired arrangement. Next, the layout is refined using the cell layout guidelines below. Finally, the material handling process is designed to present materials without interrupting the work in the cell.

Cell Layout Checklist
Guidelines for cell layout include:
- Place steps (equipment and workstations) close together with no obstacles in walking paths and no places for inventory to accumulate.

- Place the first and last steps close together to facilitate flexibility, communication, and product flow; this is often referred to as a "U-shaped" design.
- Segregate automated and manual steps to allow flexibility in distributing the work.
- Support flexibility with physical designs (utility drops, workstations on wheels, etc.).
- Dedicate tools, place them close and orient them for use.
- Make safety and good ergonomics a primary concern for the entire cell, including materials handling.
- Include equipment guidelines.

Detailed Cell Layout Example
Note that we have wrapped around the concept layout to form a detailed layout per the checklist above.

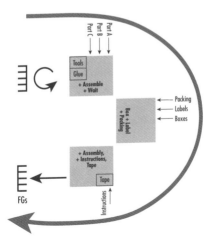

REFINING THE LAYOUT

The next steps are to:

1. Draw the operator walking pattern to test the flow.

2. Pantomime the operator motions to ensure good ergonomics.

3. Refine the layout as necessary.

STAFFING A CELL TO MEET TAKT TIME

Now that the cell has been designed to operate with a varying number of people, we need to determine the actual number of people needed in the cell, what each will do, and how the work will get done. The design will then be tested to determine if changes in demand for the product can be met.

This is necessary at this stage of cell design to ensure that our design can handle the people needed to produce what the customer needs when the customer needs it.

HOW MANY PEOPLE ARE NEEDED?

We calculated the number of people needed to cycle within Takt time for the current state by dividing the total work content by Takt time. Now the work content has been improved by doing a paper Kaizen and an ideal sequence, and the flow has been greatly improved by doing a cell design layout.

At this point, we need to allow for people variability that will inherently occur due to minor stoppages, fatigue, and variation in work content. We call this **planned cycle time (PCT)** and recommend that it be 85 percent–95 percent of Takt time.

However, you will need to determine this percentage based on past history, company agreements and policies, and other relevant factors. This is NOT an allowance for equipment downtime, setup time, or quality variations! This is for people variations.

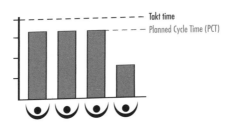

The calculation for the number of people in a cell is:

$$\text{Number of People} = \frac{\text{Total Work Content*}}{\text{Planned Cycle Time}}$$

*work content for ideal flow

The calculation for the number of people based on the ideal sequence follows. We have chosen to use 90 percent of Takt time for planned cycle time in the example.

$$\frac{\text{Total Work Content*}}{\text{PCT} = \text{Takt time} \times .90} = \frac{10\,m}{4\,m \times .9} = 2.8 \text{ people}$$

What to Do with Partial Jobs?
Then, the question arises:

What should we do with the .8 operator?

First, let's consider Lean thinking as opposed to traditional thinking. Traditionally, we have spread the work evenly among people to balance the work. However, Lean encourages us to fully load each person and expose the waste, or extra capacity, to focus on continuous improvement.

The guidelines for partial jobs are:

Fraction of person in calulation	Guideline
< .3	Do not add an additional person. Instead, further reduce waste and business value work.
.3 – .5	Hold off on an additional person for a week or two in order to evaluate whether enough waste and business value work can be removed to eliminate the need for an additional person.
> .5	Add a person, but continue efforts to reduce waste and business value work in order to eventually eliminate the need for the person.

DISTRIBUTING THE WORK

There are many options for distributing the work among the people — this is a good time to be very creative in brainstorming the different ways that work might be distributed. Any idea should be tested as completely as possible before locking in a plan. This test may have to be done with models and/or pantomiming.

Documenting the Work

The work sequence must be documented clearly. An operator balance chart can be used, or possibly a **standard work chart** that

combines the work elements, the time for each work element, the
walk distance, and a picture of the cell layout to show where each
work element occurs.

	Standard Work	Product: Widget Process:		Date: Takt time:
	Work Element	**Work**	**Walk**	
1	Move	1.0	10'	
2	Get tool	.5		
3	Part A to B	.5		
4	Part AB to C	.5		
5	Glue both	.5		
6	Wait	2.0	3'	
7	Make box	.5	1'	
8	Make label	.5	1'	
9	Label to box	.5		
10	Packing to box	.5	1'	
11	Widget to box	.5	3'	
12	Instructions	.5	1'	
13	Tape	1.0		
14	Move	1.0	4'	

Another example of a way to document clearly what is happening
in the cell when there is a combination of people and equipment
is a **combination chart**. This chart shows the time cycles for
each as well as walking time. See the example on the next page
using a shirt laundry cell. This is the shirt folding process, which
has machine and manual steps.

SAMPLE COMBINATION CHART

Work Element	Manual	Machine	Walk								
3	Fold machine (4)		30								
4	Make box (per 6)	3	1								
5	Box	6									
6	Attach order	5									
1	Move	5	2								
2	Place on machine	17									

Operator #1 can't do next element because operator's time would exceed Takt time. This element would be given to Operator #2.

CHANGING THE DEMAND

We have designed our cell for an average or median demand level. Now we need to determine how to respond to changes in the demand level.

Short term, we may

- use a finished goods supermarket to absorb fluctuations.
- use overtime or bring in part-time people.

Long term, we will need some combination of

- planned overtime (increases available time);
- additional people (spreads work content);
- additional cells.

USING PLANNED OVERTIME

In order to calculate planned overtime, we need to base our calculations on planned cycle time:

	Required Production	PCT	Required Time (sec.)	Equiv. Hours	Planned OT
Forecast	120	3.6 m	432 m		
Current	100	3.6 m	360 m		
Difference			72 m	1.2 hr.	1.0 hr.

- Required Time = Required Processing x Planned Cycle Time
  (Takt time x .90)
- Subtract current Available Time from Required Time.
- Convert difference in time into hours; round to a reasonable increment
  of planned overtime.

CHANGING THE NUMBER OF PEOPLE

Changing the output of the cell by changing the number of people
working in the cell is often referred to as **toggling**. The different
settings (number of people) are like the settings on a toggle switch.

The goal of Lean is to keep the work content for each person very
close to Takt time and have each person produce about the same
amount of product. This is referred to as **labor linearity**. We
can ask the question (and, therefore, calculate the results) two
different ways:

1. How many people do I need for my peak output and for my
   slowest output?
2. How many can I produce with one more person or one less
   person?

Let's answer each of these questions using our example cell.

How Many People Are Needed?

To calculate the number of people needed for a different demand,
we must recalculate Takt time since demand is part of the Takt
time formula. Let's say that we want to know the number of people required to build 130:

$$\frac{\text{Available time} \quad (400\ m)}{\text{Demand} \quad (130)} = 3.1\ m\ \text{Takt time}$$

Then, we can recalculate the number of people:

$$\frac{\text{Work content} \quad (10\ m)}{\text{PCT = Takt time x .90} \quad (2.8\ m)} = 3.6\ \text{people}$$

Since this is greater than .5, we would most likely add a fourth person to our cell. We'll need to go back and determine how work would be distributed with four people in the cell — this may require some redesign.

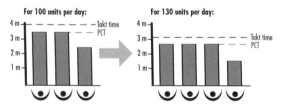

The same process can also be used to determine the number of people for a reduced demand.

Checking Labor Linearity
If we are producing 100 with 2.8 people, this equals 35.7 units per person. If we are now producing 130 with 3.6 people, this equals 36 units per person. So, the labor linearity checks out.

HOW MANY CAN I PRODUCE?

If the number of people is toggled by one (can be in either direction), how many can I produce? We can use the same two formulas to calculate this by applying simple algebra to rearrange the formulas using the data that we have. Follow these steps to answer the question using the example cell and subtracting one person to equal 1.8 people versus 2.8:

1. Solve for the new PCT by rearranging the formula for calculating the number of people:

$$\frac{\text{Work content} \quad (10 \text{ m})}{\text{Number of people} \quad (1.8 \text{ m})} = 5.6 \text{ m PCT}$$

2. Solve for the new Takt time:

$$\frac{\text{PCT} \quad (5.6 \text{ m})}{\% \text{ used} \quad (.90)} = 6.2 \text{ m Takt time}$$

3. Solve for the new demand by rearranging the formula for Takt time:

$$\frac{\text{Available time} \quad (400 \text{ m})}{\text{Takt time} \quad (6.2 \text{ m})} = 64.5 \text{ units Demand}$$

So, we can build 64 units with 1.8 people within Takt time (or PCT), or 35.5 each. The labor linearity calculation confirms our answer since it is approximately the same number of units per person as before.

REFINING THE CELL LAYOUT

All valid staffing options must be tested with the cell layout design to ensure that they are doable. It is likely that some adjustments will be needed. In some cases, the answer will be to duplicate the cell and plan to run all cells only part of the time.

STANDARDIZING FOR FLEXIBILITY

Work must be standardized before flexibility can exist. If the way we do work is constantly changing with no standards, implementing Lean will result in chaos. Standardizing for flexibility may sound like an oxymoron, but actually standard work is necessary to achieve the ultimate flexibility required for great customer service.

Standard Work must be a part of every cell design!

WHAT IS STANDARD WORK AND WHY IS IT IMPORTANT?

Standard Work is work done the same way each time, producing the same outcome each time. Documentation is necessary as a means of achieving standardization; but on its own, documentation will not achieve standardization.

Standard Work is visual; it is NOT documentation in a file or drawer or stored away electronically. The ultimate test of whether a cell has an adequate level of Standard Work is for someone to be able to perform the work correctly using ONLY the Standard Work in the cell.

Standard work originated during and after World War II at Toyota. A great need to rapidly train unskilled workers led to having the workers write their own work instructions. They learned that these instructions can't just be written at a desk or by an engineer because you work them out by trying them.

WHY IS STANDARDIZATION IMPORTANT?

- Process consistency

  When a process is stabilized, the effects of human variability are minimized.

- Process improvement

  Standardization provides a baseline, or foundation, for improvement. This supports a data-based approach such as DMAIC versus just tinkering with the process.

- Training

  Standard work provides a base for consistent training, eliminating the variation that typically occurs and speeding up effectiveness of training.

- Visual control

  When done correctly, Standard Work is visual, which helps distinguish between normal and abnormal methods.

- Safety

  Unsafe practices are formally eliminated from the process.

THREE AREAS OF STANDARDIZATION

In practice, three areas of work need to be standardized:

1. Activities of individual people, known as **Standard Work 1**

2. Connections, or the customer and supplier relationships in the process, known as **Standard Work 2**

3. Pathways, or the ways that materials and services are provided, known as **Standard Work 3**

AREAS FOR STANDARDIZATION

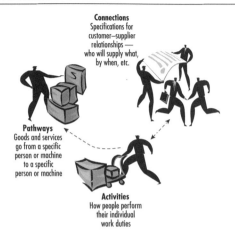

Connections
Specifications for customer–supplier relationships — who will supply what, by when, etc.

Pathways
Goods and services go from a specific person or machine to a specific person or machine

Activities
How people perform their individual work duties

STANDARD WORK 1 — INDIVIDUAL WORK

Standard Work 1 consists of a precise description of each work activity specifying data such as lead time, cycle time, Takt time, sequence of activities, materials/information necessary, quality requirements, etc.

Each activity is highly specified and includes:

- Content — specific tasks and how they should be performed
- Sequence — the order in which the tasks should be performed
- Timing — the time allowed for each task and the total time for the assigned work

Standard Work documentation does not have a set format. Different kinds of processes and tasks require different forms.

Each company should have a consistent way to document work. The important thing is not the format, but the effectiveness of the Standard Work. However, don't forget that pictures are worth a thousand words!

Ohno at Toyota believed that the people who do the work should write their own work instructions because:

- They are the "experts" in their job.
- They will rarely follow instructions written by a staff person that they don't fully understand.
- To support a particular way of doing something, they will need to understand why it is important.
- Thinking about their work and why things need to be done in a certain way is the first step in involving them in continuous improvement.
- They will keep their work instructions simple and make them understandable to co-workers.

Depending on skill and experience, Standard Work may be written by Value Stream Leaders, Value Stream Leaders jointly with employees, or by employees on their own. Coordination is necessary between shifts and with upstream and downstream processes to ensure that the Value Stream is optimized, not just one area at the expense of others.

Standard Work should be easily changed as improvements are identified. Some companies provide time each week for employees to stop producing product and update their Standard Work documentation.

Standard Work may be changed when

- schedules change.
- mix of work changes.

- problems are resolved.
- improvement ideas are implemented.

Any of these conditions could easily require a change in Takt time, which will require changes in work assignments and work sequences.

STANDARD WORK 2 — CONNECTIONS

Standard Work 2 defines the relationship between each internal customer and supplier as to what will be provided, how, and when. The objectives are to make the customer/supplier interactions more predictable, driving variability out of the Value Stream.

It consists of
- a concise agreement developed jointly by internal customers and each supplier regarding the quantity, quality, condition, and timing of the work to be passed between them.
- a simple, visual method based on pull for the customer to request work from the supplier.
- a plan for regularly auditing the agreement.

STANDARD WORK 3 — PATHWAYS

Standard Work 3 deals with the ways that material, service, or information is provided. The objective is to drive out variability from the Value Stream resulting from multiple providers and complex pathways. This will eliminate confusion and guesswork regarding the flow of work.

Standard Work 3 consists of
- defining a specific pathway for each product.
- defining a specific supplier for each product.
- providing a means to evaluate performance over time.

STANDARD WORK AND IMPROVEMENT

There can be no improvement without Standard Work! When normal and abnormal work activities are undifferentiated, waste almost inevitably occurs. Standard Work provides a basis for continuous improvement.

Standard Work Improvement Process

1. Standardize and adhere to standard.
2. Expose problems and waste.
3. Solve problems and eliminate waste.
4. Implement solutions.
5. Set new standard.
6. Repeat cycle.

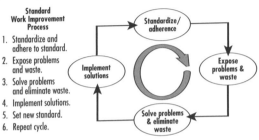

The Process to create Standard Work is:

When	Who*	What
Cell Design	Team	Create initial Standard Work; refine it as the design of the cell evolves.
Mock-up	Team and employees	Revise Standard Work as needed.
Debugging	Team and employees	Further refine Standard Work as problems are solved or improvements are made.
Production	Team and employees	Restudy the work at the end of the Debugging period and finalize Standard Work.
Approvals	Team	Cell leader and people should formally sign off on the final Standard Work.
On-going	Team Leader	Audit employees; ensure that Standard Work is kept up to date. Team leader may do the updating or, once employees are trained, assign updating to them.

* This process assumes that Team Leaders are on the cell-design team.

The steps in developing Standard Work are compared below to the steps in cell design:

Cell Design Stage	What
Single Stack	The "single stack" is the first stage in developing the overall sequence of work elements; it becomes the foundation of Standard Work.
Layout	The ideal sequence of the concept layout is a refinement of the single stack. This will be further refined as the detailed layout is developed.
Work Distribution	Initial Standard Work can be developed once the number of people has been determined and the method of work distribution established. The ideal sequence may be modified in the process of assigning work elements. An initial set of Standard Work documents should be prepared for the volume variations identified.
Mock-up	The Mock-up process should include a thorough review of the initial Standard Work.

MAINTAINING ORDER THROUGH 5S AND VISUAL WORKPLACE

The ultimate goal in a Lean Value Stream is to have a workplace that is

- self-explaining.
- self-ordering.
- self-regulating.
- self-improving.

The design of any cell, or process in general, should include the above. In other words, there are visual cues and practices in place as a part of the design that ensure consistency and order.

You will see throughout this discussion that 5S and visual workplace principles apply to electronic work as well as physical work.

Visibility can be a poster or electronic sign in the workplace or a message or sidebar on a computer screen for electronic processes. Be creative in making your visual workplace effective!

5S — WHAT, WHY, AND HOW

5S is a process to

- create workplace organization and standardization.
- achieve and sustain a clear, clean, safe, and organized workplace.
- ensure that the workplace contains only what is needed, when it is needed, and where it is needed.

WHAT IS 5S?

The 5S's consist of:

1. Sort: necessary versus unnecessary
2. Set in order: a place for everything
3. Shine: clean and ready to use
4. Standardize: maintain the gains
5. Sustain: self-discipline

The 5S circle below sums up 5S with benefits in the outer circle.

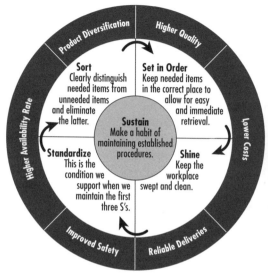

STEP 1: SORT

The underlying concept of **sort** is that unnecessary equipment, material, and supplies clutter the workplace, causing unnecessary work and motion, making it more difficult to find items that are truly needed, and sometimes making the work area less safe.

Sort also applies to electronic work. Think of all those unneeded records and e-mails that clutter computers and servers! This clutter slows down electronic systems and causes extra time and effort to be spent finding electronic files that are needed.

Don't forget to pay close attention to safety hazards as you complete the steps in sort.

1. Discard anything that isn't needed.
2. Determine a quantity needed and location for anything that is definitely needed.
3. Place items being questioned in a **red tag holding area**.
4. Resolve red tag items.

A red tag holding area is an area set aside to stage items in question. It should be out of the work area (and, out of sight). This process allows time for proper evaluation and disposition of items deemed to be unnecessary. Items are tagged with a red tag that provides pertinent information about the item (such as the category of item, what it is, where it came from), the quantity, the value, the originating date, and the eventual disposition of the item.

The idea is to get the items out of the work area to see if work can be done without them. Usually, the items are never missed! After a specified period of time, they can be discarded.

One caution, however, is: Keep in mind when the item is typically used and make sure that it is held through that period of time. For instance, if something is generally only used during the holiday rush, make sure that it is kept through one holiday season to ensure that it's not needed before discarding the item.

If an item is disposed of, determine if it's a capitalized asset and follow company procedure if it is. You will need to obtain approvals from the appropriate people, such as the Value Stream Leader, manager, and financial person. Then, determine the method of disposal. Options can include re-use elsewhere, sell it, donate it, or scrap it.

STEP 2: SET IN ORDER

The underlying concept of **set in order** is to have a place for everything and everything in its place. Everything moveable or electronic should have a designated place to be when not in use. This place should be visual, and it should be obvious when the item is not in its place.

Set in order also applies to electronic work. Have you ever wasted time just looking for certain files on a computer? Protocol is needed for filing electronic records just as we have always needed for physical records.

The steps to implement set in order are:
1. Arrange items so they are easy to find, use, and put away.
2. Apply organizing concepts.
3. Use elimination techniques.
4. Create visual controls.

For items to be easy to find, use, and put away, establish dedicated locations for each item that are well-marked and easy to access. Once again, don't forget about safety! Safety equipment should always be well-marked, in designated areas, and fully operational.

Store most frequently used physical items close-at-hand:
• Above knees, below chest
• In a location that does not disrupt the natural rhythm of the task
• Obtainable with minimum body motion
• Always in the same place so no time is wasted searching

Most frequently used electronic items should be easily accessible through special start-up programs or short cuts.

Organizing concepts include:
- Suspension:
  - Suspend tools from above, within reach of the user, using a retractable cable or balance device. This will eliminate the need to return a tool as well as the chance of misplacing it.
- Incorporation:
  - Tools and devices are smoothly integrated into the work process and are stored where they are used so there is no need to return after use.
- Elimination:
  - Finding a way to provide the function of a tool without actually using it.

Elimination techniques include:
- Tool unification:
  - Combining the function of two or more tools into one tool

    Example: Standardize all fasteners (flat *or* Phillips head).
- Tool substitution:
  - Using something other than the tool to provide the tool's function

    Example: Replace hex-head bolts with butterfly-grip bolts.
- Method substitution:
  - Replacing one method for another to improve efficiency
  - Example: Use pins or clamps instead of bolts.

Visual controls are devices which inform or indicate a condition at a glance. For example, floor painting can indicate location or labeling can indicate identity. And, of course, color coding is widely used, but only works for those of us who can see colors! So, always offer an alternate identification technique for color coding.

The following example of a tool board illustrates how visual controls can help make items easy to find, use and put away.

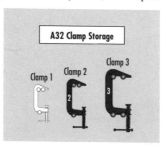

The designated location for Clamp #1 is outlined on the tool board. This makes it easy to

- determine if it is currently in-use by someone else.
- put it away when not in use.
- see if tools have been put away in a wrong location.

This concept is more challenging to implement in electronic processes, but certainly not impossible.

STEP 3: SHINE

The underlying concept of **shine** is to have everything clean and ready to use. This implies that items are cleaned after use and put away clean and ready to use again.

Shine has some application in electronic processes if we consider "cleaning up" electronic records. An example might be updating information and discarding old information within electronic records.

The steps to implement shine include:

1. Establish a **five-minute shine** routine: a small block of time each day to focus on housekeeping.

2. Develop **housekeeping checklists** consisting of shine activities that include who, when, and what area plus columns for weekly and monthly assessments.

3. Establish ongoing and specific inspection routines and provide a process for easily logging all requests for maintenance with a space for date resolved.

For each of the above steps, develop a plan that includes the following components:

Targets	Identify tools and equipment in the workplace that need to be included in the Shine process; determine cleaning and inspection frequency for each item.
Schedule	Develop a schedule and responsibilities; allocate regular time for Shine activities.
Methods	Develop standard methods for what will be done, how it will be done, and when. Incorporate inspection methods as these are developed and as cleaning becomes a routine.
Tools/Supplies	Identify required tools and supplies and ensure that they are available.
Implement	Carry out methods per the standards and schedule; audit effectiveness.

STEP 4: STANDARDIZE

The underlying concept of **standardize** is to maintain the gains. So, once the above three components of 5S are developed and tested successfully, we need to continue doing the established process. This can be the most difficult part of 5S!

Standardize is best accomplished by using aids to control what happens, when it happens, and how it happens and then focusing on prevention, or making it difficult (if not impossible) to do it wrong.

STEP 5: SUSTAIN

The underlying concept of **sustain** is self-discipline and motivation. There needs to be awareness and focus on 5S with a rewards and recognition system in place. This will result in employee satisfaction and enthusiasm for continuing the 5S efforts.

If 5S is a part of a Lean cell design, the measures for 5S are incorporated into the measures for cell performance. In any case, checklists are required for compliance, and employees must be trained to ensure a full understanding of the 5S concepts and procedures.

5S AND CELL DESIGN

5S fits with cell design principles, and an effort to implement 5S as a part of creating a cell can be fun and energizing for employees.

The following chart shows how 5S should be integrated into cell design:

	5S as an integral part of Lean Six Sigma
Sort	"Paper Red Tag" before cell layout.
Set in Order	Incorporate into the cell layout design process; implement with cell installation.
Shine	Assess equipment before cell installation; carry out as a part of cell installation.
Standardize	Incorporate into standard work for the cell.
Sustain	Tie to cell performance.

EXAMPLE OF 5S CHECKLIST

The following chart shows the progressive levels of 5S with some descriptors of each level. The key is to begin implementing 5S now — it is a critical component of every Lean implementation.

	Sort	Set in Order	Shine	Standardize	Sustain
Level 5 *Focus on Prevention*	Employees are continually seeking improvement opportunities	Documented method developed to provide continual evaluation, and process in place to implement improvements	Dependable, documented method of preventative cleaning and maintenance	Everyone is continually seeking elimination of waste, with changes documented and information shared	General appearance of a confident understanding of, and adherence to, the 5S principles
Level 4 *Focus on Consistency*	Dependable, documented method to keep the work area free of unnecessary items	Dependable, documented method to recognize visually whether items are out of place or exceed quantity limits	5S agreements understood and practiced continually	Substantial process documentation available and followed	Follow-through with 5S agreements and safety practices evident
Level 3 *Make It Visual*	Unnecessary items removed from the workplace	Designated locations marked to make organization more visible	Work and break areas plus equipment cleaned daily; visual controls established and marked	Working environment changes documented; visual control agreements established	5S agreements and safety practices developed and utilized
Level 2 *Focus on Basics*	Necessary and unnecessary items separated	Designated locations established for items	Work and break areas cleaned on a regular schedule; key items to check are identified	Methods are being improved, but changes haven't been documented	A recognizable effort has been made to improve the condition of the workplace
Level 1 *Just Beginning*	Needed and not needed items mixed throughout the workplace	Items are randomly located throughout the workplace	Workplace areas are dirty, disorganized; and key items are not marked or identified	Workplace methods are not consistently followed and are not documented	Workplace checks are randomly performed and there is no visual measurement of 5S performance

CREATING A VISUAL WORKPLACE

A visual workplace makes it easy to
- see the flow of work.
- understand the goals and how we stand in achieving them.
- train employees.
- identify problems.

Examples of a visual workplace include:

Use different colors
to identify orders received
on different days of the week

Limit Size of Inbox
to Standard WIP or
eliminate inbox completely

Limit (electronic) queue
sizes to a minimum

Use Dashboards to
display Incoming Volumes

In a visual workplace,
- the productivity objective must be visible.
- current quality levels must be visible.
- work instructions must be visible.
- improvement strategy must be visible.
- customer satisfaction level must be visible.

Visibility can be a poster or electronic sign in the workplace or a message or sidebar on a computer screen for electronic processes. Be creative in making your visual workplace effective!

IMPROVING ERGONOMICS FOR HEALTH AND SAFETY

Ergonomics is a science addressing human performance and well-being in relation to the job, equipment, tools, and the environment.

Capabilities of Employees

Job Requirements

When implementing Lean principles through cell design, we simply want to be able to recognize an injurious situation in a current or new design and get ergonomic help when needed. We are not providing enough information here to make you an ergonomics expert or practitioner!

Signs that you may need ergonomic help with a cell design are that job tasks are uncomfortable, painful, or causing injury or lack of performance.

WHAT IS ERGONOMICS?

We will focus on two aspects of ergonomics:

- **Anthropometrics** is the analysis of body size and proportion in relation to the physical environment (for example, workstation, equipment, tools).

- **Biomechanics** is the analysis of body movements and the forces acting against those movements.

ANTHROPOMETRICS

There is a great deal of variation in both size and capability among the people in any population, and any population consists of many sub-populations (gender, age, ethnicity, occupation, etc.). Therefore, the average person doesn't exist!

The usual design approach is to design for the segment of the population that is between the 5th and 95th percentile when assuming a generally normal distribution. Remember that percentiles are specific only to the populations and the specific dimensions they describe.

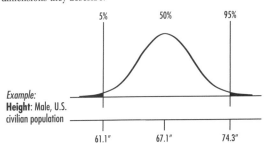

Example:
Height: Male, U.S.
civilian population

5%	50%	95%
61.1″	67.1″	74.3″

The design approach suggested is to
- provide adjustability whenever possible; examples include workstation or chair height.
- design for the extremes (5th or 95th percentile); examples include designing clearances for large people and reaches for small people.
- design for the average (50th percentile) if adjustability is not practical; an example is door handle height.

BIOMECHANICS

We typically look at biomechanics in four categories:

- Hand/wrist
- Shoulder/neck
- Back/torso
- Legs/feet

ERGONOMICS PRINCIPLES

The ergonomic principles for biomechanics include:

1. Reduce harmful positions; an example is bending or kneeling to do a task.

2. Reduce repetition rate by redesigning the work or rotating the tasks; an example is typing on a computer for long periods of time.

3. Minimize static positions in non-neutral positions. This includes isometric positions where very little movement occurs; examples include cramped or inactive postures, prolonged standing or sitting, and sedentary work.

4. Reduce excessive force; an example is designs that use knees or back to apply pressure or force.

MOTION ECONOMY

The chart below provides a checklist for our cell design. The four basic principles of **motion economy** are:

1. Reduce the number of motions.
2. Perform motions simultaneously.
3. Reduce the distance of each motion.
4. Make motions easier.

MOTION ECONOMY

Basic Principles	Motion	Work	Tools	Improvement
1. Reduce the number of motions	Both hands move symmetrically	Place tools and materials in order of use	For simple operations, or those requiring power, use devices operated by foot	Eliminate searching, choosing, carrying, placing, deliberating, and re-grasping
2. Perform motions simultaneously	Both hands start and finish at the same time	Design layouts so that both hands move simultaneously	Use devices for holding goods for a long period of time	Eliminate waiting, balancing, holding
3. Reduce the distance of each motion	Eliminate unnecessary movements	Place tools and materials to facilitate their use	Use appropriate containers for parts	Facilitate grasping and assembling
4. Make motions easier	Reduce the number of movements; combine movements where possible	Minimize the work area without obstructing body movements	Use fixing devices with fewer nuts and bolts	Reduce arm motions

MISTAKE-PROOFING THE IMPROVEMENTS

Mistake-proofing is making it easy to do right and impossible to do wrong. This is the ideal; however, making it nearly impossible or more difficult to do something wrong is a step in the right direction. We want our cell design to be as close to the ideal as possible.

Mistake-proofing is the use of low-cost devices or techniques to perform 100-percent inspection as a means of eliminating defects. It assumes that even the most conscientious and well-trained employee will occasionally make errors.

Mistake-proofing prevents errors from becoming defective products as one part of a larger inspection system.

HOW MISTAKE-PROOFING SUPPORTS LEAN

Lean and continuous flow depend on 100-percent quality. Defects cause delays, longer lead times, and extra inventory — all wastes. Mistake-proofing makes quality a part of the process instead of steps in the process (for inspections and rework).

Another term used for mistake-proofing is **Poka Yoke**. This is Japanese for: "to avoid inadvertent mistakes." The goal for mistake proofing in Lean is to design processes and procedures so that mistakes are prevented, or, at the very least, detected right after they occur.

MISTAKE-PROOFING PRINCIPLES

There are at least five mistake-proofing principles to remember when designing a new cell and/or process:

1. Control upstream, as close to the source of the defect as possible.

2. Establish controls appropriate to the severity of the potential defect.

3. Don't over-control — strive for the most efficient and economical control method.

4. Develop mistake-proofing cooperatively with operators, technicians, and engineers.

5. Don't delay improvement by over-analyzing.

DIFFERENT TYPES OF INSPECTION

The traditional approach to inspection has been to find defects. This has usually been based on sample inspections and acceptable quality levels (AQL's).

The Lean approach to inspection is to prevent defects by inspecting at or near the source. The objective, based on 100-percent inspection, is to detect and correct.

The Four Types of Inspection

Final inspection: The output is inspected at the end of the process.
- Defects can get to customer.
- Feedback and corrective action are too slow to be effective.

Successive inspection: Each person inspects 100 percent of the work of the previous person before doing his or her own operation.
- Can only check 2 or 3 characteristics
- Must provide quick feedback and stop the flow to correct
- Potential problems between workers

Self inspection: People inspect 100 percent of their own work.
- Defects are discovered at origin, allowing faster feedback and quicker corrective action.
- People may not always be objective; best used for objective characteristics.
- Must limit number of characteristics checked

Source inspection: Process inputs are inspected to discover errors in conditions that lead to defects.
- Enables action to be taken to correct errors before they produce defective product
- Sources of errors can include people, material, machines, methods, or information.

MISTAKE-PROOFING TECHNIQUES

Mistake-proofing utilizes one of three techniques: physical characteristics, constant value, or process sequence.

Physical characteristics of a product are used to detect whether it is the correct part and/or placement. A plug configured for correct polarity is a good example of both.

Constant value is used when there is a "correct" answer for comparison. Examples might be the number of steps in a process (counting) or specific edits in a software program (input only a weekday that is not a holiday).

Process sequence is used to determine that the right steps have been completed in the right order. Checklists and sensors to check steps and sequence are good examples of this technique.

MISTAKE-PROOFING METHODS

Whether for manufacturing or service or electronic (transactional) processes, mistake-proofing methods share several common features:

- Either warnings that indicate the existence of a problem or preventative controls that stop the process until the problem is resolved
- Applied as source inspection to prevent errors from occurring or as self or successive inspection to detect errors that have just occurred
- Meant to be used by the front-line employees
- Typically low cost methods

In service processes, mistake-proofing interactions with customers focus on prevention.

An example of a warning method would be the spell-check feature in word-processing programs on your computer. This feature immediately notifies you if a word is not recognized by underlining the word and/or sounding a beep. However, it is still your choice whether to change the spelling or not.

An example of a preventive, or control, method is the fueling area of your car:

1. Filling pipe insert keeps larger, leaded-fuel nozzle from being inserted.

2. Gas cap tether does not allow the motorist to drive off without the cap.

3. Gas cap is fitted with ratchet to signal proper tightness and prevent over-tightening.

Control methods are more powerful and should be used whenever possible.

MISTAKE-PROOFING STEPS

The steps to apply mistake-proofing are:

1. Identify the problem.

2. Identify the cause of the problem.

3. Determine at what level you can inspect the process (source, self, successive). If self or successive, strive over time to find a way to prevent the problem through source inspection.

4. Determine the mistake-proofing technique (physical characteristics, constant value, or process sequence).

5. Determine the method, or level of regulation (control or warning).

6. Design and implement a mistake-proofing process.

7. Try it out; refine it as necessary.

8. Train others.

9. Monitor results.

KAIZEN WORKSHOPS
Kaizen is the philosophy of continuous improvement.

WHAT IS A KAIZEN WORKSHOP?
- A means of implementing process improvements
- Short, 3–5 day events with intensive focus on one area
- A cross-functional, participative implementation approach

Workshop objectives:
- Achieve results.
- Bring new problem solving skills to the workforce.

Kaizen Workshop Principles
- There must be a willingness to improve.
- There must be a belief that improvement is always possible.
- Participants must be able to work effectively in a group.
- There must be participation from everyone.
- Everyone must be considered equal (disregard level and status).
- The process must follow a structured approach like DMAIC.
- The workshop project must be documented.
- The best solutions must be standardized.
- The best solutions must be further improved over time.

PROJECTS VS. KAIZEN WORKSHOP

	Project	**Kaizen Workshop**
Scope	Broad, negotiable	Narrow, fixed supports Value Stream Plan
Duration	Weeks or months	3–5 days
End point	When goals are achieved	End of event
Team	Operators + support staff	Operators + support staff
Team size	Max. 8 people	Max. 8 people
Training	Team + technical skills	Limited + on-the-job training
Participation	Part-time	Full-time for 3–5 days
Analysis	Developed by team	Prescribed
Focus	All phases of project	Detailed design and Implementation

ASSESSING RISKS AND PILOTING SOLUTIONS

Reducing or eliminating risks is commonly approached using FMEA (*See Measure Chapter*).

EXAMPLE OF A FMEA

A Lean Six Sigma team is charged with reducing lab turnaround time:

Step in Process	Potential Failure Mode	Potential Effect of Failure	Severity	Potential Causes	Occurrence	Current Controls	Detection	RPN
Patient gives requisition	Doesn't have requisition	Return to lab	7	Instructions not clear	3	None	10	210
Specimin is collected	Put in wrong container	Return to lab	7	New tech	7	Orientation before actual work	3	147
Specimin is logged-in and aloquotted	Data entry error	Misdiagnose	10	Illegible	2	None	10	200
Specimin is analyzed	Analyzer needs repair	Blood clots	7	No regular preventive maintenance	9	None	10	630
Results to computer	Entered to wrong patient	Misdiagnose	10	Human error	3	Active checks	2	60
Results to M.D.	Delay in sending	Return to M.D.	7	Not enough data entry clerks	8	HR planning	5	280

Highest RPN

In this example, even though the RPNs for "Specimen is logged in" and "Results to computer" are relatively low, the severity is high. The team should take action.

PLAN THE IMPLEMENTATION

With our design close to complete, we must now start considering **implementation**. We will need to plan out our implementation steps in detail. One early step will be to explain our design to others and incorporate their input through an implementation plan.

STAGES OF AN IMPLEMENTATION PLAN

Stage	Who	What
Initial Design	Loop Team	Implementation Plan, calculations, initial layout, work distribution, initial Standard Work
Mock-Up	Loop Team + operators	Introduce operators to the new design. Review objectives, process, layout, critical features, and Standard Work. Incorporate operator suggestions into the design.

SET UP CELL AND PILOT

Debug	Value Stream + Loop Team	Track production and solve problems. Observe process and make further improvements.
Sustain	Value Stream + Loop Team	Develop and implement Standard Work for support functions.

IMPLEMENTATION SCHEDULE

An Implementation Schedule along with a Story Board constitutes a persuasive Implementation Plan for your cell. An example follows.

SAMPLE IMPLEMENTATION SCHEDULE

Cell Implementation

	Step	Resp.	Status	2-Mar	9-Mar	16-Mar	23-Mar	30-Mar	6-Apr	13-Apr	20-Apr	27-Apr
1	Initial Training	Jim	100%	▓								
2	Initial design	Ron	100%	▓								
3	Mock-Up	Jim	100%		▓							
4	Fabricate parts trays	Ron	50%			▓						
5	Fabricate flow racks	Ron	50%				▓					
6	Clear out space for cell	Bill	10%				▓					
7	Build move inventory	Mary	75%					▓				
8	Relocate cell equipment	Bill						▓				
9	Standard Work training	Jim										
10	Material Handling training	Jim										
11	Debugging	Paul									▓	▓
12	FG supermarket	Jim									▓	
13	Production Kanban	Tom								▓		
14	Level Production	Tom										▓

DEVELOPING A MOCK-UP OF THE NEW DESIGN

The next step is to do a **mock-up**. A mock-up is a model of the new cell created to explain the design to the people who will run and support it and to find further improvements before full implementation. This is the step when the cell design begins to move from paper to reality.

A mock-up session includes a description of the project, the objectives, and the steps used in developing the new cell design. The design and the implementation plan is communicated to everyone involved in the mock-up.

The session also includes a thorough walk-through where the operators of the cell can go through the motions of running the cell using a conference room mock up, cardboard cut-outs, or actual (or identical) equipment arranged per the cell design.

After the Mock-Up

There are several steps that should be taken after the mock-up session:

1. Document and consider all suggestions from the mock-up.

2. Decide which suggestions should be incorporated into the final design.

3. Get final approval for the design.

4. Update everyone involved in the mock-up, including feedback on all suggestions — not just those implemented.

5. Proceed with pre-implementation items such as training, physical space, and getting needed equipment and supplies.

PILOT

WHY PILOT?

- Find flaws in the solution.
- Improve the solution before full-scale implementation.
- Find out if you are getting the results you expected.
- Good results will encourage buy-in.
- Find the parts of the process that need controls.

WHEN TO PILOT

- Pilot whenever you have not done a DOE, but especially when
  - the change is irreversible.
  - there is a chance of unforeseen negative consequences elsewhere.
  - the change incurs large costs.

TYPES OF PILOT

Product and Services:

- Limited time offers
- Release in a test market
- Rapid prototyping and early evaluation by end users
- Product alpha and beta tests

PROCESSES

- Pilot plants
- Walk-throughs, dry runs, or dress rehearsals
- Implementing only at a single location, for a particular product, on a particular line, or for a particular customer

STEPS OF A PILOT

1. Plan the pilot.
   - Data collection
   - Training
   - How to evaluate results
   - Who will be the final judge on the adequacy of the results?
2. Inform associates.
3. Conduct pilot.
4. Evaluate results.
5. Increase scope.

DEBUGGING

- Debugging is the most important part of implementation.
- It is the start-up to "running as designed."
- Debugging usually takes 2–4 weeks.
- Typical results:
  - after 1 day, 60% of target production
  - after 1 week, 80%
  - within 2 weeks, 90%

DEBUGGING — KEY POINTS

- Implement quickly after announcing the change.
- Implement improvement ideas quickly.
- Keep standard work, flowcharts, and control charts up to date.
- Note milestones to mark progress.
- After debugging, restudy work.

PERFORMANCE MEASURES

Performance measures tend to measure what the customer of the process experiences, or results. These measures are more global (lead time of the Value Stream versus processing time for one process) and tend to be longer-term measures of how the new cell is performing.

At this stage of the project, measures should tie back to the goals in the project charter as well as any other specific measures identified as being important. Three key points about determining measures are:

1. Fewer is better.
2. They must be easily reported so that status can be understood at a glance.
3. They must identify problems or problem areas to facilitate further improvements.

IMPROVE PHASE OUTPUTS

- Multiple problems solutions; those that best address the identified root cause
- Materials flow system for cell
- Standard work for the material flow system
- Pull system for cell
- Ergonomics assessment for the cell
- Full implementation plan developed, including updated stakeholder influence plan
- Process map
- Cost/benefit analysis for selected solution
- Risk analysis of the proposed solution completed

REQUIREMENTS FOR RESULTS

In Lean Six Sigma Improvement Training, we are looking for improved business performance. What produces these results? The answer is: actions. Through the DMAIC process, we have identified the actions we need to produce to get the results we intend. There are three elements that drive actions:

1. Knowledge/Skills;

2. Tools;

3. Mindset.

Belts need to understand the mindset of the people involved in the improvements being designed. Moreover, they need to be creative in moving key people up the chain of commitment in order to realize the best possible results.

CONCLUSION

At the end of the Improve Phase, the team will have assessed the risks as well as the cost/benefit of their solution. If required, a cell will have been created with attention to material flow, ergonomics, and visual management. The team will have piloted the solution and planned for full implementation. It is ready to move to the Control Phase.

Phase 5: Control

During the Improve phase, the solution was piloted, and plans
were made for full-scale implementation. Putting a solution in
place can fix a problem for the moment, but the work in Phase 5:
Control is designed to help you make sure the problem stays fixed
and that the new methods can be further improved over time.

- Control Charts
  9. Maintain Improvement
  10. Close Project

The tools most commonly used in the Control phase are:

1. Control charts (*I-MR and X-bar, R charts covered in the Measure phase*)
2. Data collection (*covered in the Measure phase*)
3. Process maps (*covered in the Define phase*)
4. Charts to compare before and after such as Frequency plots Pareto charts, etc. (*all covered in the Measure phase*)
5. Process Management Chart
6. Standardization (*covered in the Improve phase*)

ELEMENTS OF A PROCESS MANAGEMENT PLAN

A process management plan consists of four elements:

- Documentation of key processes
- Critical metrics for monitoring performance
- Data collection, analysis, and reporting plan
- Intervention and process improvement strategy

PROCESS MANAGEMENT CHART

A **process management chart** combines the graphic utility of a flowchart with the ability to show relationships on a matrix. It facilitates process management by documenting

- what the steps in the process are.
- who performs these steps and when.
- where in the process data need to be collected.
- who collects the data.
- how the data are collected and recorded.
- how often the data are collected.
- who takes action based on the data.
- where trouble-shooting procedures are documented.

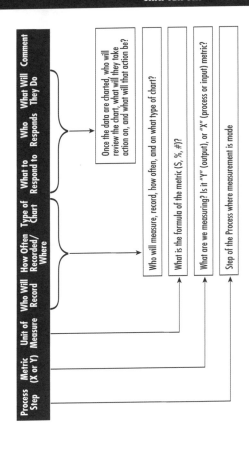

Process Step	Metric (X or Y)	Unit of Measure	Who Will Record	How Often Recorded/ Where	Type of Chart	What to Respond to	Who Responds	What Will They Do	Comment

Once the data are charted, who will review the chart, what will they take action on, and what will that action be?

Who will measure, record, how often, and on what type of chart?

What is the formula of the metric (S, %, #)?

What are we measuring? Is it "Y" (output), or "X" (process or input) metric?

Step of the Process where measurement is made

EXAMPLE OF A PROCESS MANAGEMENT CHART

Process Name: XYZ Yield							Control Plan Creation Date: 10/17/05			
Process Owner: Pete Strong							Revised Date:			
Customer: Patients, MDs, FDA, Packaging							Flowchart Name: XYZ Yield			
CTQ: % Yield							Flowchart Location: Shared Drive			
Process Step	**Metric (X or Y)**	**Unit of Measure**	**Who Will Record**	**How Often Recorded/ Where**	**Type Chart**	**What to Respond to**	**Who Responds**	**What Will They Do**	**Comments**	
Bottle	Yield Y	%	Andy	Daily	I-MR Chart	Point beyond limits	Team	Troubleshoot		
Heat	Temperature X	Degree C	Luis	2nd and 6th hour each shift	I-MR Chart	Point beyond limits	Team	Ensure temp set at 60°C		
Distill	Time X	Minutes	Phyllis	Daily	I-MR Chart	Point beyond limits	Team	Ensure distilled for 280 minutes		
Distill	Speed X	RPM	Phyllis	2nd and 6th hour each shift	I-MR Chart	Point beyond limits	Team	Ensure RPM set at 160 RPM		

CONTROL CHARTS

Ongoing monitoring is typically managed with a control chart.
One uses a control chart to

- separate common cause variation from special cause variation so that management can respond appropriately to find root causes.
- understand and predict process capability.
- measure whether intentional changes had the desired result.
- find root cause(s).
- monitor key processes to maintain the gains.

COMMON CAUSE VARIATION

Common causes

- represent everyday, random variation in a process.
- are a part of the process.
- contribute to output variation because they themselves vary.
- produce predictable levels of variation over time.
- produce all of the variation in a stable process.

SPECIAL CAUSE VARIATION

Special causes

- are not usually present.
- may come and go sporadically; may be temporary or long-term.
- appear under some particular circumstance.
- are not predictable.
- contribute to variation in an unstable process.

Tests for Special Causes

1. Any data point outside the control limits is a signal of a special cause — it signifies something unusual.

2. Eight points in a row on same side of the center line signifies a shift in the average.

3. Six points in a row, all increasing or decreasing, signifies a trend.

4. Fourteen points in a row, alternating up and down, signifies sampling from two sources, bias, or fudged data.

5. Two out of three points (on the same side) more than 2 sigma from center line signifies a shift.

6. Four out of five points (on the same side) more than 1 sigma from center line signifies a shift.

7. Fifteen points in a row within 1 sigma of center line signifies reduced common cause variation, change in operational definition, or fudged data.

8. Eight points in a row more than 1 sigma from center line signifies overcompensation, sampling from different sources, or fudged data.

Note: These last four tests are only used with continuous data and assume a normal distribution.

SPECIFICATION LIMITS VS. CONTROL LIMITS

- **Specification limits** describe what you want a process to achieve and are set by the customer, management, or engineering requirements.

- **Control limits** describe what the process is capable of achieving and are calculated from the data.

SPECIFICATION LIMITS VS. CONTROL LIMITS

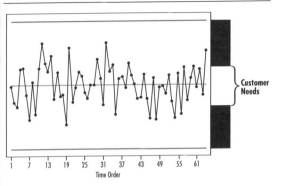

Customer Needs

Time Order

WHEN TO CALCULATE NEW CONTROL LIMITS

- Calculate new control limits when there is a permanent change to the process, based upon
  - statistical evidence, such as 8 data points above or below the centerline.
  - standardization of a planned process change.
- Collect at least 24 new data points before making the new limits permanent.

WHAT TO LOOK FOR WHEN USING CONTROL CHARTS
- The chart is being used concurrently with the process.
- Charts are posted.
- Charts are up-to-date.
- Comments are written on charts.
  - Process changes
  - Verified special causes with corrective action

COMMON MISTAKES WHEN USING CONTROL CHARTS
- The chart is not created correctly.
  - Wrong type of chart for type of data
  - Wrong formula used
- The chart is not up-to-date.
  - Missing data
  - Process changes not documented
  - Control limits and average not updated
- Responses are inappropriate.
  - Rewarding or attempting to explain individual points when there are no special-cause signals
  - Special-cause signals ignored
- There are spec limits on the chart instead of control limits

CONTROL CHARTS FOR DISCRETE DATA (p, np, c, u CHARTS)
There are various types of control charts.
- Different types of control charts are used for different types of data.
- They all differentiate special cause from common cause variation.

©2007 Rath & Strong/Aon Management Consulting

- They all use control limits to indicate if an individual data value is due to a special cause.
- Each type of control chart should have at least 24 data points to calculate control limits.

TYPES OF DATA: RECAP

- Continuous data are obtained by measuring.
  - Examples: Length, pressure, time
- Discrete data are obtained by counting events that meet certain criteria.
  - Examples: Number of defective units, number of spots on the carpet

Discrete Attribute Data:
Equal Sample Sizes, np or p-chart

Day	(n) Units Sampled per Day	(np) # Rejects	(p) Proportion of Rejects
Mon	50	5	0.10
Tue	50	3	0.06
Wed	50	6	0.12
Thu	50	8	0.16
Fri	50	2	0.04
Mon	50	1	0.02
Tue	50	4	0.08
Wed	50	6	0.12
Thu	50	3	0.06
Fri	50	7	0.14

For np chart   *For p chart*

Discrete Attribute Data:
Unequal Sample Sizes, p-chart

Day	(n) Units Sampled per Day	(np) # Rejects	(p) Proportion of Rejects
Mon	200	20	0.10
Tue	176	12	0.07
Wed	212	24	0.11
Thu	180	32	0.18
Fri	145	8	0.06
Mon	195	4	0.02
Tue	173	16	0.09
Wed	205	24	0.12
Thu	190	12	0.06
Fri	137	28	0.20

Misleading to chart these values

Better representation of the process

Discrete Count Data:
Equal Opportunities, c-chart

Day	(c) # Computer crashes per day
Mon	6
Tue	3
Wed	1
Thu	0
Fri	3
Mon	1
Tue	5
Wed	2
Thu	4
Fri	1

You cannot count non-crashes,
but it is possible for one
computer to crash
more than once
in a day.

The day is the
equal opportunity.

Discrete Count Data:
Unequal Opportunities, u-chart

Month	(a) Days in a month	(c) # Computer crashes	(u) # Computer crashes per month
Jan	31	24	0.77
Feb	28	12	0.43
Mar	31	4	0.13
Apr	30	0	0.00
May	31	12	0.39
Jun	30	4	0.13
Jul	31	20	0.65
Aug	31	8	0.26
Sep	30	16	0.53
Oct	31	4	0.13

a = area of opportunity   count misleading   count/area of opportunity

CONTROL CHART FORMULAS FOR DISCRETE DATA

Chart	Distribution	Control Limit Formula
p chart	Binomial	$\bar{p} \pm 3\sqrt{\dfrac{\bar{p}(1-\bar{p})}{n}}$
np chart	Binomial	$n\bar{p} \pm 3\sqrt{n\bar{p}(1-\bar{p})}$
c chart	Poisson	$\bar{c} \pm 3\sqrt{\bar{c}}$
u chart	Poisson	$\bar{u} \pm 3\sqrt{\dfrac{\bar{u}}{a}}$

Charts for Discrete Data Assumptions
p (or np) chart assumptions based on the binomial distribution:
  • There are only two attributes (e.g., late or not late).
  • Each sample is expected to have the same proportion of items with the attribute.
  • Attribute occurrence is independent from item to item.

c (or u) chart assumptions based on the Poisson distribution:
  • One can count occurrences, but not non-occurrences.
  • Occurrence is expected less than 10% of the time.
  • Occurrences are independent.

EWMA CHARTS

Exponentially Weighted Moving Average (EWMA) charts are used for detecting small shifts quickly. The moving average smoothes the variation.

EWMA charts
- consist of continuous, time-ordered, sub-grouped or individual data.
- detect small shifts in the process average.
- can predict the next value in an unstable process.
- EWMA charts are not helpful in identifying a single point out-side the limit.

EXAMPLES: IMPORTANT SMALL SHIFTS

A Small Shift in...	Profoundly Affects:
• Interest rate	• Debt ratio
• Process yield	• Profit
• Pharmaceutical precision	• Disease survival rate

How the EWMA Chart Works
- Points weighted with the most weight are assigned to the most recent point.
- Weight decreases exponentially moving backwards in time.

Sequence	Output (Y)	Calculations	EWMA (weight 0.2)
1	90	(0.2) 90 + (0.8) 92	91.6
2	91	(0.2) 91 + (0.8) 91.6	91.5
3	94	(0.2) 94 + (0.8) 91.5	92.0
4	95	(0.2) 95 + (0.8) 92	92.6
5	92	(0.2) 92 + (0.8) 92.6	92.5
6	97	(0.2) 97 + (0.8) 92.5	93.4
7	91	(0.2) 91 + (0.8) 93.4	92.9
8	98	(0.2) 98 + (0.8) 92.9	93.9
9	90	(0.2) 90 + (0.8) 93.9	93.1

Current value given 20% of the weight; previous EWMA value given 80%. The first calculation uses either the historical average or an average of all the data (in this case, 92)

Actual observations are plotted on the Individuals Chart

The weight of 0.2 is typical, but it can be changed

Values resulting from the EWMA calculations are plotted on an EWMA chart

HOW THE EWMA CHART WORKS

SUMMARY OF CONTROL CHARTS

- Choose the type of control chart based upon
    - the type of data.
    - whether data were collected individually or in subgroups.
- Use statistical software to construct the control chart.
- Assess the control limits.
    - If too wide or narrow,
        * try an I-MR chart.
        * try a transformation.
    - Omit special causes from calculation of limits.
- Look for special causes and take appropriate actions.
- Maintain the control chart:
    - Plot points as they occur.
    - Take action immediately.
    - Recalculate limits when appropriate.

SELECTING A CONTROL CHART

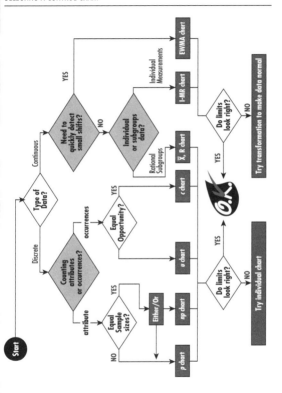

SUMMARY TABLE OF CONTROL CHARTS

Situation	Chart Used	Control Limit Calculations	Comments
Counting Defects Number of defects, errors, or flaws: # of errors/mo. # of breakdowns/wk. # of flaws on a laptop case	**c chart**	$\bar{c} \pm 3\sqrt{\bar{c}}$	Always plot data in time order if there is a natural chronological sequence; use a **c** or **u chart** on non-time-ordered data such as location.
	u chart	$\bar{u} \pm 3\sqrt{\dfrac{\bar{u}}{a}}$	Use when the area of opportunity varies; **Examples**: reorganization doubles the number of employees in one division, doubling the area of risk; different computers have different case sizes, so areas where scratches can occur varies.
Fraction of "defectives" Fraction of orders not filled within 24 hrs.	**p chart**	$\bar{p} \pm 3\sqrt{\dfrac{\bar{p}(1-\bar{p})}{n}}$	**Notation:** n = the number of units per subgroup x = the number of units found defective p = the proportion of defectives (= x/n)
Fractions of applications not processed perfectly the first time through (first-pass yield)	**np chart**	$\bar{np} \pm 3\sqrt{\bar{np}(1-\bar{p})}$	• The **np chart** is used only when **n is roughly constant**. • For **p or np charts**, the fraction must be based on counts • For proportions of measurements use an I-MR chart

SUMMARY TABLE OF CONTROL CHARTS

Situation	Chart Used	Control Limit Calculations	Comments
Variables data, one figure at a time Sales, expenses, total	**I-MR chart**	$\bar{X} \pm 2.66\bar{R}$ or $\bar{X} \pm 3.14\tilde{R}$	• Use with any time-based data • Less powerful in detecting special causes than more specialized charts **Note: Do not use $\bar{X} \pm 3s$ where:** $s = \sqrt{\sum \dfrac{(\bar{X} - X)^2}{n-1}}$ since special causes could be masked.
Variables data, sets of measurements	**$\bar{X}$, R chart**	$\bar{\bar{X}} \pm A_2\bar{R}$ For R chart: UCL = $D_3\bar{R}$ LCL = $D_4\bar{R}$	• Used when the same variable is measured repeatedly to check measurement stability • May be used for charts of moving averages (such as a chart of running three-month averages of customer satisfaction) **Notation:** n = number of items in subgroup (e.g., n = 3 measurements/day) X = individual measurement $\bar{X}$ = average of the subgroup $\bar{\bar{X}}$ = average of the averages $\bar{R}$ = average range of values in the subgroup

ASSUMPTIONS FOR CONTROL CHARTS

Control Chart	Distribution	Assumptions
I-MR EWMA $\bar{X}$, R charts	Normal	Data are distributed symmetrically around the mean with a peak of the curve at the mean
p	Binomial	p remains constant across subgroups and occurrrences are independent
c	Poisson	Probability of occurrence is constant and occurrences are rare and independent

CONTINUOUS IMPROVEMENT AND PROJECT CLOSURE

The **continuous improvement** process
- displays before and after data.
- recalculates process sigma or Cpk.
- identifies additional opportunities.
- establishes a process auditing schedule that
  - allows for immediate identification and resolution of problems.
  - prevents backsliding and keeps the improvement effort moving forward.
- is part of management's Standard Work.

PERFORMANCE MEASURES
Using Visual Measures to Improve

A problem awareness board like the one shown below tracks the cell's adherence to plan (or Takt time) and logs problems that may have been encountered. This type of visual measure should be visible to everyone in the cell; and, as we said before, a support plan needs to be in place to solve these problems.

This type of visual measure is useful not only during implementation and debugging, but also when the cell is fully operational.

Per Day: 690			Takt time: 40 sec.
Time	**Plan**	**Actual**	**Problem**
7–8	90	90	
8–9	90	83	Bender downtime (electrical)
9–10	75	59	Bender downtime (cont'd) Crimping quality
10–11	90	86	Out of parts (fermules)
11–12	15		

Hourly plan vs. actual; could also track cumulative plan vs. actual

PROJECT CLOSURE OBJECTIVES

- Provide a clear ending for the project.
- Assess results.
- Identify lessons learned for the next time.
- Transfer responsibility for continued operation and improvement to the process owner.
- Identify opportunities for replicating results.

CONTROL PHASE OUTPUTS

- Statistical data that the improved process is now under control
- A draft for a monitoring system that will ensure that the results are sustained and that changes in the process can be easily detected
- Documented procedures for the process
- Evidence that the solution has been integrated into the day-to-day workflow, and can be sustained
- Recalculated process sigma
- Evidence that the team has considered the "people elements" in sustaining the results

CONCLUSION

The team can show that the new process has been standardized and is in control. A new process sigma has been calculated. A monitoring system is in place that will detect changes and, therefore, hold the gains.

As was stated at the outset, customers are interested in cost, quality, and time. The DMAIC methodology using Lean and Six Sigma tools is an extremely powerful way to provide customers with the highest quality, at the lowest cost, in the least amount of time. ∎
